ENGINEERING MECHANICS

THIRD EDITION

DYNAMICS STUDY PACK

FREE BODY DIAGRAM WORKBOOK
BY PETER SCHIAVONE
WORKING MODEL SIMULATION CD
BEDFORD AND FOWLER
PROBLEMS WEBSITE
BEDFORD AND FOWLER

BEDFORD   FOWLER

Prentice
Hall

PRENTICE HALL, Upper Saddle River, NJ 07458

Acquisitions Editor: Eric Svendsen
Managing Editor: David A. George
Production Editor: Blake Cooper
Supplement Cover Manager: Paul Gourhan
Supplement Cover Designer: PM Workshop Inc.
Manufacturing Buyer: Lisa McDowell

© 2002 by Prentice-Hall, Inc.
Upper Saddle River, NJ 07458

Printed in the United States of America

10 9 8 7 6 5 4 3 2 1

ISBN   0-13-093235-3

Prentice-Hall International (UK) Limited, London
Prentice-Hall of Australia Pty. Limited, Sydney
Prentice-Hall Canada, Inc., Toronto
Prentice-Hall Hispanoamericana, S.A., Mexico City
Prentice-Hall of India Private Limited, New Delhi
Pearson Education Asia Pte. Ltd., Singapore
Prentice-Hall of Japan, Inc., Tokyo
Editora Prentice-Hall do Brazil, Ltda., Rio de Janeiro

Foreword

This Study Pack was designed to help students improve their study skills. It consists of three study components—a free body diagram workbook, a Visualization CD based on Working Model Software, and an access code to a website with over 500 sample Statics and Dynamics problems and solutions.

- Free Body Diagram Workbook—Prepared by Peter Schiavone of the University of Alberta. This workbook begins with a tutorial on free body diagrams and then includes 50 practice problems of progressing difficulty, with complete solutions. Further "strategies and tips" help students understand how to use the diagrams in solving the accompanying problems.

- Working Model CD—This CD contains pre-set simulations of text examples that include questions for further exploration. Simulations are powered by the Working Model Engine and were created with actual artwork from the text to enhance their correlation to the text. A set of questions associated with each simulation can be found in Appendix A of this workbook. The CD will install when inserted in your drive. Make sure to note and copy the case-sensitive serial number that appears. You will need it to complete the installation. During use, some systems may launch Microsoft Windows Media Player instead of Working Model. If this occurrs:

  1. Select "Start" and choose "Working Model 2D 5.0" from your program menu.
  2. After Working Model launches, select "File" and "Open" and explore your CD drive.
  3. Simulations for the text are located on the CD within the "WM Files" folder.

- Problems Website—Located at http://www.prenhall.com/bedford. This website contains 500 sample Statics and Dynamics problems for students to study. Problems are keyed to each chapter of the text and contain complete solutions. All problems are supplemental and do not appear in the third edition. Student access codes are printed on the inside cover of the Free Body Diagram Workbook. To access this site, go to http://www.prenhall.com/bedford, choose the link for the Problems Website, and follow the on-line directions to register. This site also contains an unprotected section with multiple choice and True/False check-up questions by Karim Nohra of the University of South Florida.

- On-Line Homework—http://www.prenhall.com/bedford also provides randomized homework problems. Your instructor may require you to use this feature of the site. The access code printed on the inside cover of this workbook provides access. Complete instructions are found at the site.

Preface

A thorough understanding of how to draw and use a free-body diagram is absolutely essential when solving problems in mechanics.

This workbook consists mainly of a collection of problems intended to give the student practice in drawing and using free-body diagrams when solving problems in dynamics.

All the problems are presented as tutorial problems with the solution only partially complete. The student is then expected to complete the solution by 'filling in the blanks' in the spaces provided. This gives the student the opportunity to build free-body diagrams in stages and extract the relevant information from them when formulating equations of motion. Earlier problems provide students with partially drawn free-body diagrams and lots of hints to complete the solution. Later problems are more advanced and are designed to challenge the student more. The complete solution to each problem can be found at the back of the page. The problems are chosen from two-dimensional theories of particle and rigid body dynamics. Once the ideas and concepts developed in these problems have been understood and practiced, the student will find that they can be extended in a relatively straightforward manner to accommodate the corresponding three-dimensional theories.

The book begins with a brief primer on free-body diagrams: where they fit into the general procedure of solving problems in dynamics and why they are so important. Next follows a few examples to illustrate ideas and then the workbook problems.

For best results, the student should read the primer and then, beginning with the simpler problems, try to complete and understand the solution to each of the subsequent problems. The student should avoid the temptation to immediately look at the completed solution over the page. This solution should be accessed only as a last resort (after the student has struggled to the point of giving up), or to check the student's own solution after the fact. The idea behind this is very simple:

*We learn most when we actually **do** the thing we are trying to learn.*

In other words, reading through someone else's solution to a problem is not the same as actually working through the problem yourself. In the former, the student gains information, in the latter the student gains knowledge. For example, how many people learn to swim or drive a car by reading an instruction manual?

Consequently, since this book is based on *doing*, the student who persistently solves the problems in this book will ultimately gain a thorough, usable knowledge of how to draw and use free-body diagrams.

P. Schiavone

1

Basic Concepts in Dynamics

Engineering mechanics is divided into two areas: statics and dynamics. *Statics* deals with the equilibrium of bodies, that is, those that are either at rest (if originally at rest) or move with constant velocity (if originally in motion). *Dynamics* is concerned with the accelerated motion of bodies. The study of dynamics is itself divided into two parts: *kinematics*, which treats only the geometric aspects of motion and *kinetics* which is concerned with the analysis of forces causing the motion. Free-body diagrams play a significant role in solving problems in *kinetics*.

In mechanics, real bodies (e.g. planets, cars, planes, tables, crates, etc) are represented or *modeled* using certain idealizations which simplify application of the relevant theory. In this book we refer to only two such models:

- **Particle or Point in Space.** *A particle* has mass but no size/shape. When an object's size/shape can be neglected so that only its mass is relevant to the description of its motion, the object can be modeled as a particle. This is the same thing as saying that the motion of the object can be modeled as the motion of a *point in space* (the point itself representing the center of mass of the moving object). For example, the size of an aircraft is insignificant when compared to the size of the earth and therefore the aircraft can be modeled as a particle (or point in space) when studying its three dimensional motion in space.

- **Rigid Body.** *A rigid body* represents the next level of modeling sophistication after the particle. That is, a rigid body is a collection of particles (which therefore has mass) which has a significant size/shape but this size/shape cannot change. In other words, when an object is modeled as a rigid body, we assume that any deformations (changes in shape) are relatively small and can be neglected. Although any object does deform as it moves, if its deformation is small, *you can approximate its motion by modeling it as a rigid body*. For example, the actual deformations occurring in most structures and machines are relatively small so that the rigid body assumption is suitable in these cases.

1.1 Equations of Motion

1.1.1 Equation of Motion for a Particle

When a system of forces acts on a particle, the equation of motion may be written in the form

$$\Sigma \mathbf{F} = m\mathbf{a} \tag{1.1}$$

where $\Sigma \mathbf{F}$ is the vector sum of all the external forces acting on the particle and m and $\mathbf{a}$ are, respectively, the mass and acceleration of the particle.

Successful application of the equation of motion (1.1) requires a complete specification of all the known and unknown external forces ($\Sigma\mathbf{F}$) that act on the object. The best way to account for these is to draw the object's *free-body diagram*: a sketch of the object *freed* from its surroundings showing *all* the (external) forces that *act* on it. In dynamics problems, since the resultant of these external forces produces the vector $m\mathbf{a}$, in addition to the free-body diagram, a *kinetic diagram* is often used to represent graphically the magnitude and direction of the vector $m\mathbf{a}$. In other words, the equation (1.1) can be represented graphically as:

$$\boxed{\textbf{Free-body Diagram = Kinetic Diagram}}$$

Of course, whenever the equation of motion (1.1) is applied, it is required that measurements of the acceleration be made from a *Newtonian* or inertial frame of reference. *Such a coordinate system does not rotate and is either fixed or translates in a given direction with a constant velocity (zero acceleration).* This definition ensures that the particle's acceleration measured by observers in two different inertial frames of reference will always be the *same*.

1.1.2 Equation of Motion for a System of Particles

The equation of motion (1.1) can be extended to include a *system of particles* isolated within an enclosed region in space:

$$\Sigma\mathbf{F} = m\mathbf{a}_G \tag{1.2}$$

This equation states that the sum of external forces ($\Sigma\mathbf{F}$) acting on the system of particles is equal to the total mass m of the particles multiplied by the acceleration $\mathbf{a}_G$ of its mass center G. Since, in reality, all particles must have a finite size to possess mass, equation (1.2) justifies application of the equation of motion to a *body* that is represented as a single particle.

1.1.3 Equations of Motion for a Rigid Body

Since rigid bodies, by definition, have a definite size/shape, their motion is governed by *both* translational and rotational quantities. The translational equation of motion for (the mass center of) a rigid body is basically equation (1.2). That is,

$$\Sigma\mathbf{F} = m\mathbf{a}_G \tag{1.2}$$

In this case, the equation (1.2) states that the sum of all the external forces acting on the body is equal to the body's mass m multiplied by the acceleration $\mathbf{a}_G$ of its mass center G.

The rotational equation of motion for a rigid body is given by

$$\Sigma\mathbf{M}_G = I_G\boldsymbol{\alpha} \tag{1.3}$$

which states that the sum of the applied couple moments and moments of all the external forces computed about a body's mass center $G(\Sigma\mathbf{M}_G)$ is equal to the product of the moment of inertia of the body about an axis passing through $G(I_G)$ and the body's angular acceleration $\boldsymbol{\alpha}$.

Alternatively, equation (1.3) can be re-written in more general form as:

$$\Sigma\mathbf{M}_P = I_G\boldsymbol{\alpha} + \Sigma(\mathbf{M}_a)_P \tag{1.4}$$

Here, $\Sigma\mathbf{M}_P$ represents the sum of the applied couple moments and the external moments taken about a general point $P(\neq G)$ and $\Sigma(\mathbf{M}_a)_P$ represents the moments generated by the components of the vector $m\mathbf{a}_G$ about the point P.

When applying the equations of motion (1.2)–(1.4), one should always draw a *free-body diagram* in order to account for the terms involved in ($\Sigma\mathbf{F}$), ($\Sigma\mathbf{M}_G$), or ($\Sigma\mathbf{M}_P$). The *kinetic diagram* is also useful in that it accounts graphically for the acceleration components $m\mathbf{a}_G$ and the term $I_G\boldsymbol{\alpha}$, and it is especially convenient when used to determine the moment terms $\Sigma(\mathbf{M}_a)_P$ generated by the components of the vector $m\mathbf{a}_G$ about the point P (when using (1.4)).

2

Free-Body Diagrams: the Basics

2.1 Free-Body Diagram: Particle

The equation of motion (1.1) is used to analyze the motion of *an object* (modeled as a particle) when subjected to an unbalanced force system. The first step in this analysis is to draw the *free-body* diagram to identify the external forces ($\Sigma\mathbf{F}$) acting on the object. The free-body diagram is simply a sketch of the object *freed* from its surroundings showing *all* the (external) forces that *act* on the object. The diagram focuses your attention on the object of interest and helps you identify all the external forces ($\Sigma\mathbf{F}$) acting. Once the free-body diagram is drawn, it may be helpful to draw the corresponding *kinetic diagram*. This diagram accounts graphically for the acceleration components (components of the vector a) on the object. Taken together, these diagrams provide (in graphical form) all the information that is needed to write down the equation of motion (1.1).

EXAMPLE 2.1

The crate A shown in Figure 1, is released from rest. Its mass is $m_A = 50$ kg and the coefficient of kinetic friction between the crate and the inclined surface is $\mu_k = 0.15$. Draw the free-body and kinetic diagrams of crate A as it slides down the plane.

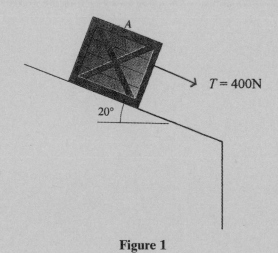

Figure 1

Solution

The free-body diagram of crate A is shown in Figure 2(a). Notice that once the crate is *separated* or *freed* from the system (= crate + plane), forces which were previously internal to the system become external to the crate. For example, in Figure 2(a), such a force is the force of friction *acting on the crate*. The kinetic diagram is shown in Figure 2(b). In this case, the diagram shows the components of the crate's acceleration vector **a**.

Next, we present a formal procedure for drawing free-body diagrams for a particle or system of particles. ◄

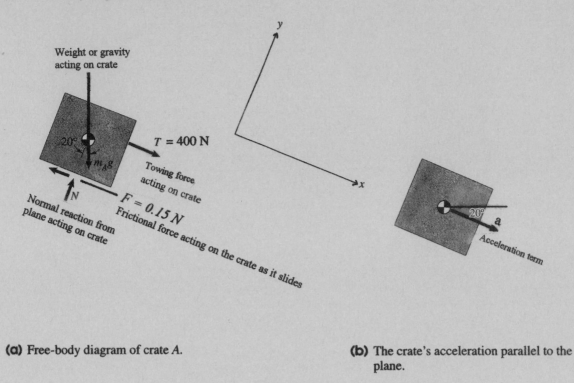

(a) Free-body diagram of crate A.

(b) The crate's acceleration parallel to the plane.

Figure 2

2.1.1 Procedure for Drawing a Free-Body Diagram: Particle.

1. *Select* the inertial coordinate system. Most often, rectangular or x, y-coordinates are chosen to analyze problems for which the particle has *rectilinear motion*. If this occurs, one of the axes should extend in the direction of motion.

2. *Identify the object you wish to isolate* from the system. This choice is often dictated by the particular forces of interest.

3. *Draw the outlined shape of the isolated object.* Imagine the object to be isolated or cut free from the system of which it is a part.

4. *Show all external forces acting on the isolated object.* Indicate on this sketch all the external forces that act on the object. These forces can be *active forces*, which tend to set the object in motion, or they can be *reactive forces* which are the result of the constraints or supports that prevent motion. This stage is crucial: it may help to trace around the object's boundary, carefully noting each external force acting on it. Don't forget to include the weight of the object (unless it is being intentionally neglected).

5. *Identify and label each external force acting on the (isolated) object.* The forces that are known should be labeled with their known magnitudes and directions. Use letters to represent the magnitudes and arrows to represent the directions of forces that are unknown.

6. *The direction of a force having an unknown magnitude can be assumed.*

7. *The direction and sense* of the particle's acceleration **a** should also be established. If the sense of its components is unknown, assume they are in the same direction as the positive inertial coordinate axes. The acceleration may be sketched on the x, y-coordinate system or it may be represented on the *kinetic diagram*.

2.1.2 Using the Free-Body Diagram: Equations of Motion

The equations of motion (1.1) or (1.2) are used to solve problems which require a relationship between the forces acting on a particle and the accelerated motion they cause. Whenever (1.1) or (1.2) is applied, the unknown force and acceleration components should be identified and an equivalent number of equations should be written. If further equations are required for the solution, kinematics may be considered.

The *free-body diagram* is used to identify the unknown force and the *kinetic diagram* the unknown acceleration components acting on the particle. The subsequent procedure for solving problems once the free-body (and, if necessary, the kinetic) diagram for the particle is established, is therefore as follows:

---

1. If the forces can be resolved directly from the free-body diagram, apply the equations of motion in their scalar component form. For example:

$$\Sigma F_x = ma_x \text{ and } \Sigma F_y = ma_y \tag{2.1}$$

2. Components are positive if they are directed along a positive axis and negative if they are directed along a negative axis.

3. If the particle contacts a rough surface, it may be necessary to use the frictional equation, which relates the coefficient of kinetic friction to the magnitudes of the frictional and normal forces acting at the surfaces of contact. Remember that the frictional force always acts on the free-body diagram such that it opposes the motion of the particle *relative to the surface it contacts*.

4. If the solution yields a negative result, this indicates the sense of the force is the reverse of that shown/assumed on the free-body diagram.

EXAMPLE 2.2

In Example 2.1, the diagrams established in Figure 2 give us a "pictorial representation" of all the information we need to apply the equations of motion (2.1) to find the unknown force **N** and the acceleration **a**. In fact, taking the positive x-direction to be parallel to the plane ($\searrow +$) and the positive y-direction to be perpendicular to the plane ($\nearrow +$),the equations of motion (2.1) when applied to crate A (regarded as a particle—since its shape is not important in the motion under consideration) are:

For Crate A: $\searrow + \Sigma F_x = ma_x :$ $400 + 50 \, g \sin 20° - F = 50 a_x$
$\nearrow + \Sigma F_y = ma_y :$ $N - 50 \, g \cos 20° = 0$

Two equations, 3 unknowns: use the frictional equation to relate F to N and obtain a third equation:

Frictional Equation (block is sliding): $F = 0.15 \, N.$

Solving these three equations yields

$$N = 460.92 \, \text{N}, \quad a_x = 9.97 \, \text{m/s}^2 \quad \text{Ans.}$$

The directions of each of the vectors N and **a** is shown in the free-body diagram above (Figure 2).   ◀

2.2 Free-Body Diagram: Rigid Body

The equations of motion (1.2) and (1.3) (or (1.4)) are used to determine unknown forces, moments and acceleration components acting *on an object* (modeled as a rigid body) subjected to an unbalanced system of forces and moments. The first step in doing this is again to draw the *free-body* diagram of the object to identify *all* of the external forces and moments acting on it. The procedure for drawing a free-body diagram in this case is much the same as that for a particle with the main difference being that now, because the object has "size/shape", it can support also external couple moments and moments of external forces.

2.2.1 Procedure for Drawing a Free-Body Diagram: Rigid Body

1. Select the inertial x, y or n, t coordinate system. This will depend on whether the body is in rectilinear or curvilinear motion.
2. Imagine the body to be isolated or 'cut free' from its constraints and connections and sketch its outlined shape.
3. Identify all the external forces and couple moments that act on the body. Those generally encountered are:
   (a) Applied loadings
   (b) Reactions occurring at the supports or at points of contact with other bodies.
   (c) The weight of the body (applied at the body's center of gravity G)
   (d) Frictional forces
4. The forces and couple moments that are known should be labeled with their proper magnitudes and directions. Letters are used to represent the magnitudes and direction angles of forces and couple moments that are *unknown*. Indicate the dimensions of the body necessary for computing the moments of external forces. In particular, if a force or couple moment has a known line of action but unknown magnitude, the arrowhead which defines the sense of the vector can be assumed. The correctness of the assumed sense will become apparent after solving the equations of motion for the unknown magnitude. By definition, the magnitude of a vector is *always positive*, so that if the solution yields a *negative* scalar, the minus sign indicates that the vector's sense is *opposite* to that which was originally assumed.
5. *The direction and sense* of the acceleration of the body's mass center $\mathbf{a}_G$ should also be established. If the sense of its components is unknown, assume they are in the same direction as the positive inertial coordinate axes. The acceleration may be sketched on the x, y-coordinate system or it may be represented as the $\mathbf{a}_G$ vector on the *kinetic diagram*. This will also be helpful for "visualizing" the terms needed in the moment sum $\Sigma(M_a)_P$ of equation (1.4), since the kinetic diagram accounts graphically for the components $(\mathbf{a}_G)_x$, $(\mathbf{a}_G)_x$, or $(\mathbf{a}_G)_t$, $(\mathbf{a}_G)_n$.

Important Points

- Internal forces are never shown on the free-body diagram since they occur in equal but opposite collinear pairs and therefore cancel each other out.
- The weight of a body is an external force and its effect is shown as a single resultant force acting through the body's center of gravity G.
- *Couple moments* can be placed anywhere on the free-body diagram since they are *free vectors*. Forces can act at any point along their lines of action since they are *sliding vectors*.

EXAMPLE 2.3

Draw the free-body and kinetic diagrams for the 60-kg crate. A horizontal force of 700 N is applied to the crate as shown and the coefficient of kinetic friction between the crate and the ground is $\mu_k = 0.3$.

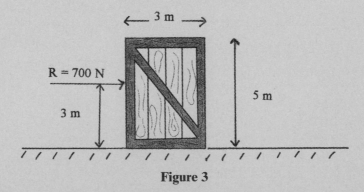

Figure 3

Solution

Here, since the force **R** can cause the crate to either slide or to tip over, we model the crate as a rigid body. This model allows us to account for the effects of moments arising from **R** and any other external forces. We begin by assuming that the crate slides so that the frictional equation yields $F = \mu_k$, $N_C = 0.3N_C$. Also, the normal force $\mathbf{N}_C$ acts at O, a distance s (where $0 < s \leq 1.5$ m) from the crate's center line. Note that the line of action of $\mathbf{N}_C$ does not necessarily pass through the mass center G $(s = 0)$, since $\mathbf{N}_C$ must counteract the tendency for tipping caused by **R**.

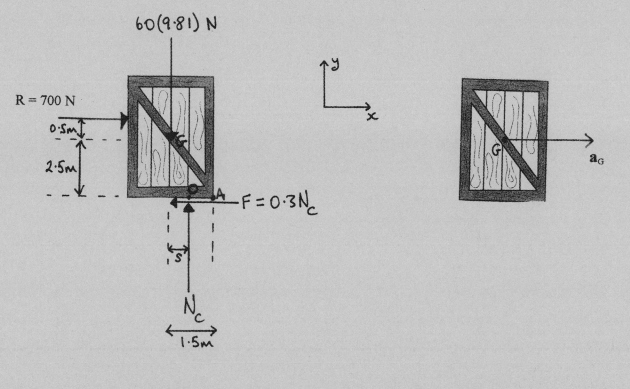

Free-body Diagram   Kinetic Diagram

Figure 4

(Note that had we assumed that the crate tips, then the normal force $\mathbf{N}_C$ would have been assumed to act at the corner point A and the frictional equation would take the form $F \leq 0.3N_C$).   ◄

2.2.2 Using the Free-Body Diagram: Equations of Motion

The procedure for solving kinetic problems for a rigid body once the free-body diagram is established, is as follows:

- Apply the three equations of motion (1.2)–(1.3). To simplify the analysis, the moment equation (1.3) may be replaced by the more general equation (1.4) where the point P is usually located at the intersection of the lines of action of as many unknown forces as possible.

- If the body contacts a rough surface, it may be necessary to use the frictional equation, which relates the coefficient of kinetic friction to the magnitudes of the frictional and normal forces acting at the surfaces of contact. Remember that the frictional force always acts on the free-body diagram such that it *opposes the motion of the body relative to the surface it contacts*.

- Use kinematics if the velocity and position of the body are to be determined.

EXAMPLE 2.4

Find the acceleration of the crate in Example 2.3.

Solution

Using the free-body diagram in Figure 4, the equations of motion are (taking counterclockwise as positive):

$$\rightarrow +\Sigma F_x = m(a_G)_x : \qquad 700\text{ N} - 0.3N_C = (60\text{ kg})(a_G)_x$$

$$\uparrow +\Sigma F_y = m(a_G)_y : \qquad N_C - 589.2\text{ N} = 0$$

$$\Sigma M_G = I_G\alpha : \qquad -700\text{ N}(0.5\text{ m}) + N_C(s) - 0.3N_C(2.5\text{ m}) = 0$$

Solving, we obtain $\quad N_C = 589.2\text{ N} \uparrow, s = 1.34\text{ m}, a_G = 8.7\text{ m/s}^2 \rightarrow \quad Ans.$

Since $s = 1.34\text{ m} < 1.5\text{ m}$, indeed the crate slides as originally assumed (otherwise the problem would have to be reworked with the assumption that tipping occurred).   ◄

3

Problems

3.1 Free-Body Diagrams in Particle Kinetics

Problem 3.1

The 2−kg collar A is initially at rest on the smooth horizontal bar. At $t = 0$ (where t is time),the collar is subjected to a constant horizontal force with magnitude $F = 4$ N as shown. Draw the free-body and kinetic diagrams for the collar.

Solution

1. The size/shape of the collar does not affect the (rectilinear) motion under consideration. Consequently, we assume that the collar has *negligible size* so that it can be modelled as a particle.

2. Imagine the collar to be separated or detached from the system (collar + bar).

3. The (detached) collar is subjected to three *external* forces. They are caused by:

   i.   **ii.**

   iii.

4. Draw the free-body diagram of the (detached) collar showing all these forces labeled with their magnitudes and directions. Include any other information e.g. angles, lengths etc which may help when formulating the equations of motion.

5. The acceleration of the collar is along the bar. Show this on a kinetic diagram or on the inertial coordinate system chosen in the free-body diagram.

Problem 3.1

The 2—kg collar A is initially at rest on the smooth horizontal bar. At $t = 0$ (where t is time), the collar is subjected to a constant horizontal force with magnitude $F = 4$ N as shown. Draw the free-body and kinetic diagrams for the collar.

Solution

1. The size/shape of the collar does not affect the (rectilinear) motion under consideration. Consequently, we assume that the collar has *negligible size* so that it can be modelled as a particle.

2. Imagine the collar to be separated or detached from the system (collar + bar).

3. The (detached) collar is subjected to three *external* forces. They are caused by:

      i. Collar's Weight   **ii. Bar's Reaction to Collar**

      iii. Force with Magnitude $F = 4$ N

4. Draw the free-body diagram of the (detached) collar showing all these forces labeled with their magnitudes and directions. Include any other information e.g. angles, lengths etc which may help when formulating the equations of motion.

5. The acceleration of the collar is along the bar. Show this on a kinetic diagram or on the inertial coordinate system chosen in the free-body diagram.

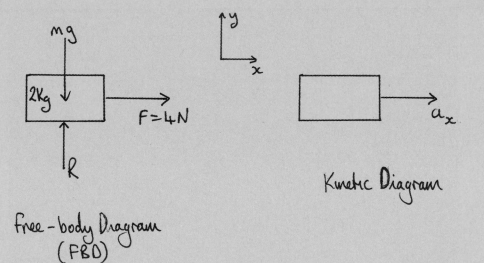

Problem 3.2

Suppose in Problem 3.1, the bar is no longer smooth and the coefficient of kinetic friction between the collar and the bar is $\mu_k = 0.1$. Draw the free-body and kinetic diagrams for the collar and use them to determine how fast the collar is moving and how far the collar has travelled after one second.

Solution

1. The size/shape of the collar does not affect the (rectilinear) motion under consideration. Consequently, we assume that the collar has *negligible size* so that it can be modelled as a particle.

2. Imagine the collar to be separated or detached from the system (collar + bar).

3. The (detached) collar is subjected to four *external* forces

      i.   **ii.**

     iii.   **iv.**

4. Draw the free-body diagram of the (detached) collar showing all these forces labeled with their magnitudes and directions. Include any other information e.g. angles, lengths etc which may help when formulating the equations of motion.

5. Establish an appropriate $xy-$axes system and draw the corresponding kinetic diagram.

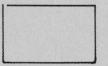 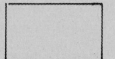

6. Using the $xy-$axes system on the free-body diagram, write down the equations of motion for the collar in the $x-$ and $y-$ directions:

   $$+\rightarrow \; \sum F_x = ma_x :$$

   $$+\uparrow \; \sum F_y = ma_y :$$

7. Solve for the acceleration of the collar.

8. Integrate the acceleration of the collar to obtain the desired speed and distance:

Problem 3.2

Suppose in Problem 3.1, the bar is no longer smooth and the coefficient of kinetic friction between the collar and the bar is $\mu_k = 0.1$. Draw the free-body and kinetic diagrams for the collar and use them to determine how fast the collar is moving and how far the collar has travelled after one second.

Solution

1. The size/shape of the collar does not affect the (rectilinear) motion under consideration. Consequently, we assume that the collar has *negligible size* so that it can be modelled as a particle.

2. Imagine the collar to be separated or detached from the system (collar + bar).

3. The (detached) collar is subjected to four *external* forces. They are caused by:

   i. **Collar's Weight**

   ii. **Bar's Reaction to Collar**

   iii. **Force with Magnitude** $F = 4$ N

   iv. **Friction Force on Collar**

4. Draw the free-body diagram of the (detached) collar showing all these forces labeled with their magnitudes and directions. Include any other information e.g. angles, lengths etc which may help when formulating the equations of motion.

5. Establish an appropriate $xy-$axes system and draw the corresponding kinetic diagram.

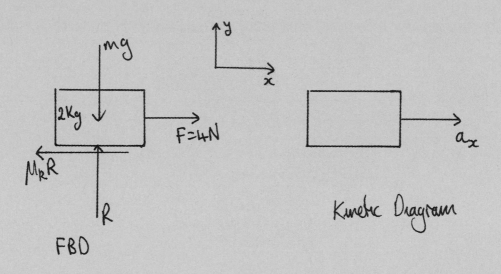

6. Using the $xy-$axes system on the free-body diagram, write down the equations of motion for the collar in the $x-$ and $y-$ directions:

$$\rightarrow + \sum F_x = ma_x : 4 - \mu_k R = 2a_x \Leftrightarrow 4 - (0.1)\, R = 2a_x$$

$$+\uparrow \ \sum F_y = ma_y : R - mg = 0 \Leftrightarrow R - 2g = 0$$

7. Solve for the acceleration of the collar. $a_x = 1.02$ m/s^2, $R = 19.62$ N

8. Integrate the acceleration of the collar to obtain the desired speed and distance:

   $v_x = a_x t, x = a_x \frac{t^2}{2}$. Now let $t = 1$ s to obtain $v_x = 1.02$ m/s, $x = 0.51$ m.

Problem 3.3

The 20−lb collar A is initially at rest on the smooth bar. At $t = 0$ (where t is time), it is subjected to a constant force with magnitude $F = 10$ lb as shown. Draw the free-body and kinetic diagrams for the collar.

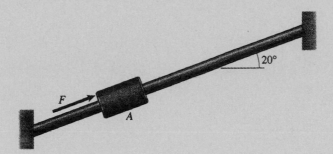

Solution

1. The size/shape of the collar does not affect the (rectilinear) motion under consideration. Consequently, we assume that the collar has *negligible size* so that it can be modelled as a particle.
2. Imagine the collar to be separated or detached from the system (collar + bar).
3. The (detached) collar is subjected to three *external* forces. They are caused by:

   i.   **ii.**

   iii.

4. Draw the free-body diagram of the (detached) collar showing all these forces labeled with their magnitudes and directions. Include any other information e.g. angles, lengths etc which may help when formulating the equations of motion.
5. The acceleration of the collar is along the bar. Show this on a kinetic diagram or on the inertial coordinate system chosen in the free-body diagram.

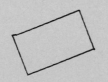

Problem 3.3

The 20—lb collar A is initially at rest on the smooth bar. At $t = 0$ (where t is time), it is subjected to a constant force with magnitude $F = 10$ lb as shown. Draw the free-body and kinetic diagrams for the collar.

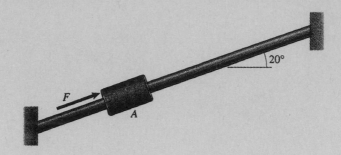

Solution

1. The size/shape of the collar does not affect the (rectilinear) motion under consideration. Consequently, we assume that the collar has *negligible size* so that it can be modelled as a particle.

2. Imagine the collar to be separated or detached from the system (collar + bar).

3. The (detached) collar is subjected to three *external* forces. They are caused by:

   i. Collar's Weight   **ii. Bar's Reaction to Collar**

   iii. Force with Magnitude $F = 10$ lb

4. Draw the free-body diagram of the (detached) collar showing all these forces labeled with their magnitudes and directions. Include any other information e.g. angles, lengths etc which may help when formulating the equations of motion.

5. The acceleration of the collar is along the bar. Show this on a kinetic diagram or on the inertial coordinate system chosen in the free-body diagram.

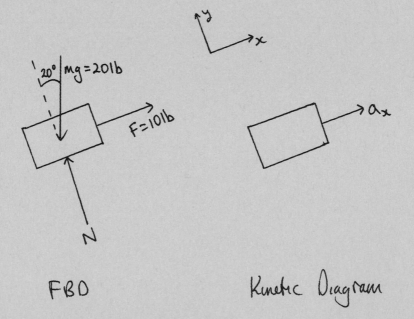

Problem 3.4

Suppose in Problem 3.3, the bar is no longer smooth and the coefficients of static and kinetic friction between the collar and the bar are $\mu_s = \mu_k = 0.1$. Draw the free-body and kinetic diagrams for the collar and use them to determine if the collar moves. If the collar does move, find how fast the collar is moving and how far the collar has travelled after one second.

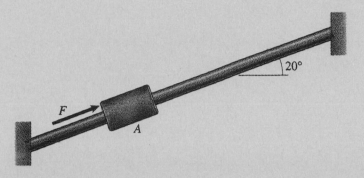

Solution

1. The size/shape of the collar does not affect any subsequent (rectilinear) motion under consideration. Consequently, we assume that the collar has *negligible size* so that it can be modelled as a particle.

2. Imagine the collar to be separated or detached from the system (collar + bar).

3. The (detached) collar is subjected to four *external* forces. They are caused by:

   i.   **ii.**

   iii.   **iv.**

4. Draw the free-body diagram of the (detached) collar showing all these forces labeled with their magnitudes and directions. Include any other information e.g. angles, lengths etc which may help when formulating the equations of motion.

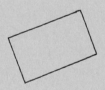

5. To determine if the collar moves, assume a static collar and determine whether the friction force necessary to keep the collar stationary is greater than the static friction force available. If this is the case, then the collar moves. Otherwise the collar remains stationary.

   Establish an appropriate xy−axes system such that x is parallel to the bar and y is normal to the bar. Write down the *equations of equilibrium* for the collar in the $x-$ and $y-$ directions:

   $$+\rightarrow \ \sum F_x = ma_x:$$

   $$+\uparrow \ \sum F_y = ma_y:$$

6. By solving these equations, deduce that there is insufficient (static) frictional force available to prevent the collar from moving under the given conditions

7. Using the $xy-$axes system on the free-body diagram, write down the *equations of motion* for the collar in the $x-$ and $y-$ directions:

$$+\rightarrow \sum F_x = ma_x :$$

$$+\uparrow \; \sum F_y = ma_y :$$

8. Solve for the acceleration components of the collar.

9. Integrate the acceleration components of the collar to obtain the desired speed and distance:

Problem 3.4

Suppose in Problem 3.3, the bar is no longer smooth and the coefficients of static and kinetic friction between the collar and the bar are $\mu_s = \mu_k = 0.1$. Draw the free-body and kinetic diagrams for the collar and use them to determine if the collar moves. If the collar does move, find how fast the collar is moving and how far the collar has travelled after one second.

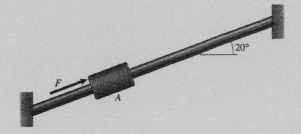

Solution

1. The size/shape of the collar does not affect any subsequent (rectilinear) motion under consideration. Consequently, we assume that the collar has *negligible size* so that it can be modelled as a particle.
2. Imagine the collar to be separated or detached from the system (collar + bar).
3. The (detached) collar is subjected to four *external* forces. They are caused by:

   i. Collar's Weight   **ii. Bar's Reaction to Collar**

   iii. Force with Magnitude $F = 10$ lb   **iv. Friction Force on Collar**

4. Draw the free-body diagram of the (detached) collar showing all these forces labeled with their magnitudes and directions. Include any other information e.g. angles, lengths etc which may help when formulating the equations of motion.

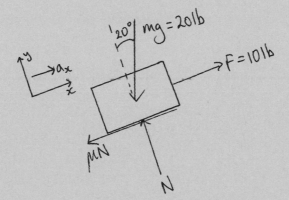

5. To determine if the collar moves, assume a static collar and determine whether the friction force necessary to keep the collar stationary is greater than the static friction force available. If this is the case, then the collar moves. Otherwise the collar remains stationary. Establish an appropriate xy−axes system such that x is parallel to the bar and y is normal to the bar. Write down the *equations of equilibrium* for the collar in the $x-$ and $y-$ directions:

$$+\rightarrow \ \sum F_x = ma_x : F - mg \sin\theta - f_{REQ} = 0 \Leftrightarrow 10 - 20 \sin 20° - f_{REQ} = 0$$

$$+\uparrow \ \sum F_y = ma_y : N - mg \cos\theta = 0 \Leftrightarrow N - 20 \cos 20° = 0$$

6. By solving these equations, deduce that there is insufficient (static) frictional force available to prevent the collar from moving under the given conditions. Solving, we obtain:

$$f_{REQ} = 3.16 \text{ lb}, \ N = 18.79 \text{ lb, and } f_{AVAIL} = \mu_s N = (0.1)(18.79) = 1.88 \text{ lb} < f_{REQ}. \text{ Hence the collar moves.}$$

7. Using the xy−axes system on the free-body diagram, write down the *equations of motion* for the collar in the $x-$ and $y-$ directions:

$$+\rightarrow \ \sum F_x = ma_x : F - mg \sin\theta - \mu_k N = ma_x \Leftrightarrow 10 - 20 \sin 20° - 0.1N = \frac{20}{g} a_x$$

$$+\uparrow \ \sum F_y = ma_y : N - mg \cos\theta = ma_y \Leftrightarrow N - 20 \cos 20° = 0$$

8. Solve for the acceleration components of the collar. $a_x = 2.06$ ft/s^2

9. Integrate the acceleration components of the collar to obtain the desired speed and distance:
$v_x = a_x t$, $x = a_x \frac{t^2}{2}$. Now let $t = 1s$ to obtain $v_x = 2.06$ ft/s, $x = 1.03$ ft.

Problem 3.5

The jeep tows the box which has a weight of 200 lb. The coefficient of kinetic friction between the box and the ground is μ_k. Draw free-body and kinetic diagrams for the box as it slides.

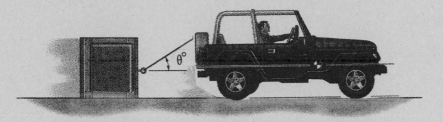

Solution

1. The size/shape of the box does not affect the (rectilinear) motion under consideration. Consequently, we assume that the box has *negligible size* so that it can be modelled as a particle.

2. Imagine the box to be separated or detached from the system (box + jeep + ground).

3. The (detached) box is subjected to four *external* forces. They are caused by:

   i.   **ii.**

   iii.   **iv.**

4. Draw the free-body diagram of the (detached) box, showing all these forces labeled with their magnitudes and directions. Include any other information e.g. angles, lengths etc which may help when formulating the equations of motion.

5. Draw the corresponding kinetic diagram.

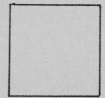

Problem 3.5

The jeep tows the box which has a weight of 200 lb. The coefficient of kinetic friction between the box and the ground is μ_k. Draw free-body and kinetic diagrams for the box as it slides.

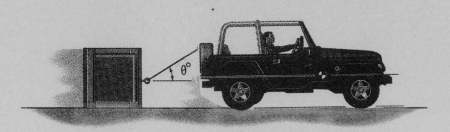

Solution

1. The size/shape of the box does not affect the (rectilinear) motion under consideration. Consequently, we assume that the box has *negligible size* so that it can be modelled as a particle.

2. Imagine the box to be separated or detached from the system (box + jeep + ground).

3. The (detached) box is subjected to four *external* forces. They are caused by:

   i. **Weight of Box**   ii. **Towing Force in Cable**

   iii. **Frictional Force**   iv. **Reaction from Surface**

4. Draw the free-body diagram of the (detached) box, showing all these forces labeled with their magnitudes and directions. Include any other information e.g. angles, lengths etc which may help when formulating the equations of motion.

5. Draw the corresponding kinetic diagram.

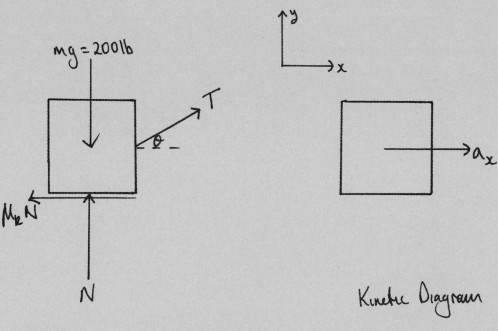

Problem 3.6

The 150—lb person rides an elevator which has an upward acceleration a relative to the earth. Draw free-body and kinetic diagrams for the person.

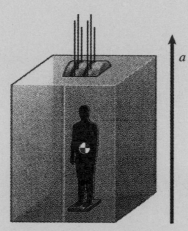

Solution

1. The size/shape of the person does not affect the (rectilinear) motion under consideration. Consequently, we assume that the person has *negligible size* and can be modelled as a particle.

2. Imagine the person to be separated or detached from the system.

3. The (detached) person is subjected to two *external* forces. They are caused by:

   i.   ii.

4. Draw the free-body diagram of the (detached) person showing these forces labeled with their magnitudes and directions. Include any other information e.g. angles, lengths etc which may help when formulating the equations of motion.

5. Draw the corresponding kinetic diagram.

Problem 3.6

The 150—lb person rides an elevator which has an upward acceleration *a* relative to the earth. Draw free-body and kinetic diagrams for the person.

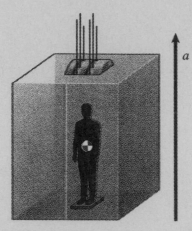

Solution

1. The size/shape of the person does not affect the (rectilinear) motion under consideration. Consequently, we assume that the person has *negligible size* and can be modelled as a particle.

2. Imagine the person to be separated or detached from the system.

3. The (detached) person is subjected to two *external* forces. They are caused by:

   i. Person's Weight   **ii. Reaction of Supporting Surface**

4. Draw the free-body diagram of the (detached) person showing these forces labeled with their magnitudes and directions. Include any other information e.g. angles, lengths etc which may help when formulating the equations of motion.

5. Draw the corresponding kinetic diagram.

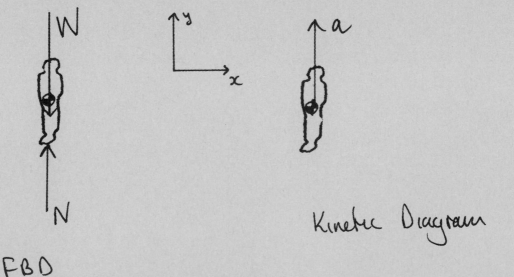

Problem 3.7

The rocket travels straight up at low altitude. Its weight at the present time is 200 kip, and the thrust of its engine is 270 kip. An onboard accelerometer indicates that the rocket's acceleration is 10 ft/s² upward. Draw a free-body diagram for the rocket and use it to determine the magnitude of the aerodynamic drag on the rocket.

Solution

1. The size/shape of the rocket does not affect the (rectilinear) motion under consideration. Consequently, we assume that the rocket has *negligible size* so that it can be modelled as a particle.
2. Imagine the rocket to be separated or detached from the system.
3. The (detached) rocket is subjected to three *external* forces. They are caused by:

   i.   ii.

   iii.

4. Draw the free-body diagram of the (detached) rocket showing all these forces labeled with their magnitudes and directions. Include any other information e.g. angles, lengths etc which may help when formulating the equations of motion.
5. Draw the corresponding kinetic diagram.

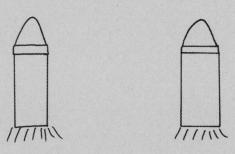

6. Using the $xy-$axes system on the free-body diagram, write down the equation of motion in the $y-$ direction:

   $+\uparrow \quad \sum F_y = ma_y :$
7. Solve for the magnitude of the drag.

Problem 3.7

The rocket travels straight up at low altitude. Its weight at the present time is 200 kip, and the thrust of its engine is 270 kip. An onboard accelerometer indicates that the rocket's acceleration is 10 ft/s^2 upward. Draw a free-body diagram for the rocket and use it to determine the magnitude of the aerodynamic drag on the rocket.

Solution

1. The size/shape of the rocket does not affect the (rectilinear) motion under consideration. Consequently, we assume that the rocket has *negligible size* so that it can be modelled as a particle.

2. Imagine the rocket to be separated or detached from the system.

3. The (detached) rocket is subjected to three *external* forces. They are caused by:

   i. Rocket's Weight   **ii. Thrust Force**

   iii. Drag Force

4. Draw the free-body diagram of the (detached) rocket showing all these forces labeled with their magnitudes and directions. Include any other information e.g. angles, lengths etc which may help when formulating the equations of motion.

5. Draw the corresponding kinetic diagram.

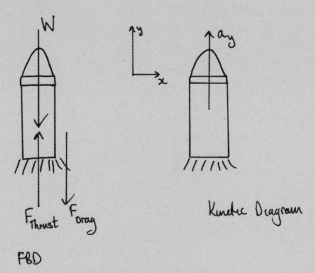

6. Using the xy−axes system on the free-body diagram, write down the equation of motion in the $y-$ direction:
$$+\uparrow \quad \sum F_y = ma_y : F_{Thrust} - F_{Drag} - W = ma_y \Leftrightarrow 270000 - F_{Drag} - 200000 = \frac{20000}{32.17}\,(10)$$

7. Solve for the magnitude of the drag. $F_{Drag} = 7830$ lb.

Problem 3.8

The combined weight of the motorcycle and rider is 360 lb. The coefficient of kinetic friction between the motorcycle's tires and the road is $\mu_k = 0.8$. If the rider spins the rear (drive) wheel, the normal force between the rear wheel and the road is 250 lb, and the horizontal force exerted on the front wheel by the road is negligible. Draw a free-body diagram of the combined motorcycle and rider use it to determine the resulting horizontal acceleration.

Solution

1. Imagine the combined motorcycle + rider to be separated or detached from the system.
2. The combined motorcycle + rider is subjected to three *external* forces. They are caused by

   i.   ii.

   iii.

3. Draw the free-body diagram of the (detached) combined motorcycle and rider showing all these forces labeled with their magnitudes and directions. Include any other information e.g. angles, lengths etc which may help when formulating the equations of motion. What is the direction of the acceleration vector for the combined motorcycle and rider . Show this on a kinetic diagram or on the inertial coordinate system chosen in the free-body diagram.

4. Using the $xy-$axes system on the free-body diagram, write down the equation of motion in the (horizontal) $x-$ direction:
   $$+\rightarrow \sum F_x = ma_x :$$

5. Solve for the magnitude of the acceleration:

Problem 3.8

The combined weight of the motorcycle and rider is 360 lb. The coefficient of kinetic friction between the motorcycle's tires and the road is $\mu_k = 0.8$. If the rider spins the rear (drive) wheel, the normal force between the rear wheel and the road is 250 lb, and the horizontal force exerted on the front wheel by the road is negligible. Draw a free-body diagram of the combined motorcycle and rider use it to determine the resulting horizontal acceleration.

Solution

1. Imagine the combined motorcycle + rider to be separated or detached from the system.
2. The combined motorcycle + rider is subjected to three *external* forces. They are caused by

    i. Combined Weight of Motorcycle + Rider   **ii. Friction**

    iii. Normal Force Between Rear Wheel and Road

3. Draw the free-body diagram of the (detached) combined motorcycle and rider showing all these forces labeled with their magnitudes and directions. Include any other information e.g. angles, lengths etc which may help when formulating the equations of motion. What is the direction of the acceleration vector for the combined motorcycle and rider . Show this on a kinetic diagram or on the inertial coordinate system chosen in the free-body diagram.

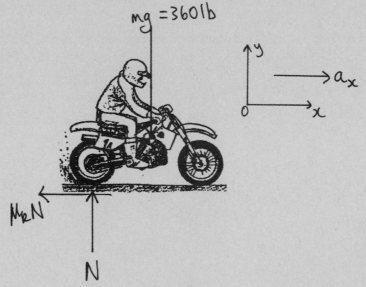

4. Using the $xy-$axes system on the free-body diagram, write down the equation of motion in the (horizontal) $x-$ direction:

$$\xrightarrow{+} \ \sum F_x = ma_x : \mu_k N = ma_x \Leftrightarrow (0.8)\,250 = \tfrac{360}{32.17}a_x$$

5. Solve for the magnitude of the acceleration: $a_x = 17.87$ ft/s^2.

Problem 3.9

The bucket B weighs 400 lb and the acceleration of its center of mass is $\mathbf{a} = -30\mathbf{i} - 10\mathbf{j}$ (ft/sec^2). Draw free-body and kinetic diagrams for the bucket and use them to find the x and $y-$ components of the total force exerted on the bucket by its supports.

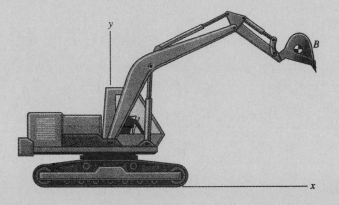

Solution

1. The bucket has *negligible size* so that it can be modelled as a particle.
2. Imagine the bucket to be separated or detached from the system.
3. The (detached) bucket is subjected to three *external* forces. They are caused by:

      i.   ii.

     iii.

4. Draw the free-body diagram of the (detached) bucket showing all these forces labeled with their magnitudes and directions. Include any other information e.g. angles, lengths etc which may help when formulating the equations of motion. Show the corresponding acceleration components on a kinetic diagram or on the inertial coordinate system chosen in the free-body diagram.

5. Using the $xy-$axes system on the free-body diagram, write down the equation of motion in the $x-$ and $y-$ directions:

   $+\rightarrow \ \sum F_x = ma_x :$

   $+\uparrow \ \ \sum F_y = ma_y :$

6. Solve for the required force components.

Problem 3.9

The bucket B weighs 400 lb and the acceleration of its center of mass is $\mathbf{a} = -30\mathbf{i} - 10\mathbf{j}$ (ft/sec^2). Draw free-body and kinetic diagrams for the bucket and use them to find the x and $y-$ components of the total force exerted on the bucket by its supports.

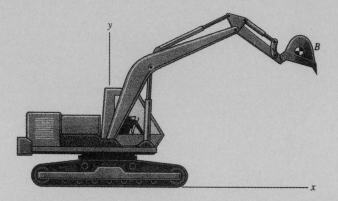

Solution

1. The bucket has *negligible size* so that it can be modelled as a particle.
2. Imagine the bucket to be separated or detached from the system.
3. The (detached) bucket is subjected to three *external* forces. They are caused by:

   i. Bucket's Weight   **ii. (2) Forces Exerted on the Bucket by its Supports**

   iii.

4. Draw the free-body diagram of the (detached) bucket showing all these forces labeled with their magnitudes and directions. Include any other information e.g. angles, lengths etc which may help when formulating the equations of motion. Show the corresponding acceleration components on a kinetic diagram or on the inertial coordinate system chosen in the free-body diagram.

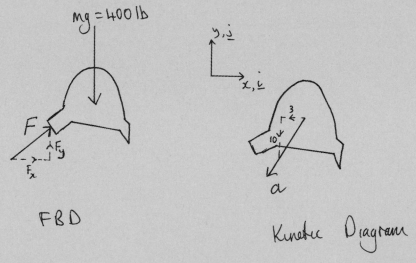

5. Using the $xy-$axes system on the free-body diagram, write down the equation of motion in the $x-$ and $y-$ directions:

   $+\rightarrow \sum F_x = ma_x : F_x = ma_x \Leftrightarrow F_x = \frac{400}{32.17}(-30) = -373.0$

   $+\uparrow \sum F_y = ma_y : F_y - W = ma_y \Leftrightarrow F_y - 400 = \frac{400}{32.17}(-10)$

6. Solve for the required force components. $F_x = -373.0$ lb, $F_y = 275.7$ lb

Problem 3.10

At the instant shown, the 11000 kg airplane is subjected to the thrust $T = 110$ kN, lift $L = 260$ kN and the drag $D = 34$ kN. Use a free-body diagram of the airplane to determine the magnitude of its acceleration.

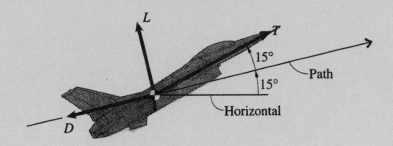

Solution

1. Imagine the airplane to be separated or detached from the system.
2. The (detached) airplane is subjected to four *external* forces. They are caused by:

   i.   **ii.**

   iii.   **iv.**

3. Draw the free-body diagram of the (detached) airplane showing all these forces labeled with their magnitudes and directions. Include any other information e.g. angles, lengths etc which may help when formulating the equations of motion. Show the corresponding acceleration components on a kinetic diagram or on the inertial coordinate system chosen in the free-body diagram

4. Using the xy–axes system on the free-body diagram, write down the equations of motion in the x and $y-$ directions:

$$\sum F_x = ma_x :$$

$$\sum F_y = ma_y :$$

5. Solve for the required acceleration components and hence the magnitude of the acceleration of the aircraft.

Problem 3.10

At the instant shown, the 11000 kg airplane is subjected to the thrust $T = 110$ kN, lift $L = 260$ kN and the drag $D = 34$ kN. Use a free-body diagram of the airplane to determine the magnitude of its acceleration.

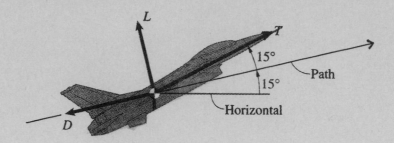

Solution

1. Imagine the airplane to be separated or detached from the system.
2. The (detached) airplane is subjected to four *external* forces. They are caused by:

    i. Thrust Force   **ii. Lift Force**

    iii. Airplane's Weight   **iv. Drag Force**

3. Draw the free-body diagram of the (detached) airplane showing all these forces labeled with their magnitudes and directions. Include any other information e.g. angles, lengths etc which may help when formulating the equations of motion. Show the corresponding acceleration components on a kinetic diagram or on the inertial coordinate system chosen in the free-body diagram

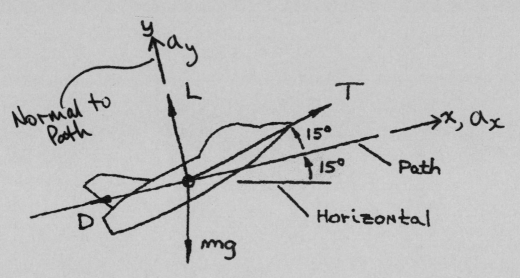

4. Using the $xy-$axes system on the free-body diagram, write down the equations of motion in the x and $y-$ directions:

$$\sum F_x = ma_x : T\cos 15^\circ - D - mg\sin 15^\circ = ma_x$$

$$\sum F_y = ma_y : L + T\sin 15^\circ - mg\cos 15^\circ = ma_y$$

5. Solve for the required acceleration components and hence the magnitude of the acceleration of the aircraft.

$$a_x = 4.03 \ \text{m/s}^2, a_y = 16.75 \ \text{m/s}^2, |\mathbf{a}| = \sqrt{a_x^2 + a_y^2} = 17.23 \ \text{m/s}^2.$$

Problem 3.11

Each box weighs 50 lb. Draw the free-body and kinetic diagrams for each box as they slide from their initial positions (the coefficient of kinetic friction between the boxes and the surface is μ_k).

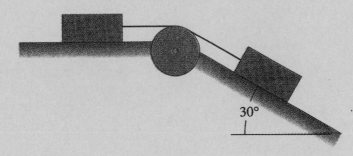

Solution

1. The size/shape of the each box does not affect the (rectilinear) motion under consideration. Consequently, we assume that the boxes have *negligible size* so that each can be modelled as a particle.

2. Imagine each box to be separated or detached from the system.

3. Each box is subjected to four *external* forces.

4. Draw the free-body diagram of each (detached) box showing all these forces labeled with their magnitudes and directions. Include any other information e.g. angles, lengths etc which may help when formulating the equations of motion.

5. Show the acceleration of each block on a kinetic diagram or on the inertial coordinate system chosen in the corresponding free-body diagram.

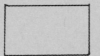

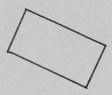

Problem 3.11

Each box weighs 50 lb. Draw the free-body and kinetic diagrams for each box as they slide from their initial positions (the coefficient of kinetic friction between the boxes and the surface is μ_k).

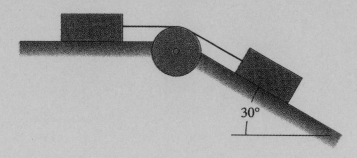

Solution

1. The size/shape of the each box does not affect the (rectilinear) motion under consideration. Consequently, we assume that the boxes have *negligible size* so that each can be modelled as a particle.
2. Imagine each box to be separated or detached from the system.
3. Each box is subjected to four *external* forces.
4. Draw the free-body diagram of each (detached) box showing all these forces labeled with their magnitudes and directions. Include any other information e.g. angles, lengths etc which may help when formulating the equations of motion.
5. Show the acceleration of each block on a kinetic diagram or on the inertial coordinate system chosen in the corresponding free-body diagram.

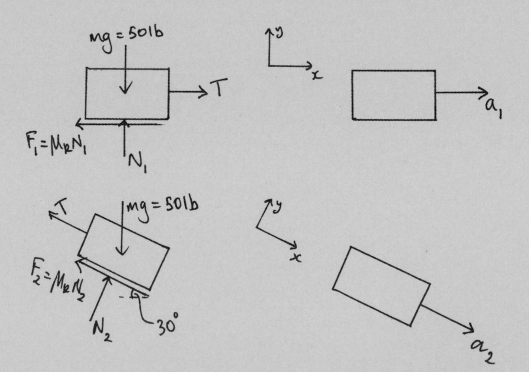

Problem 3.12

The boat weighs 2600 lb with its passengers. It is moving in a circular path of radius $R = 80$ ft at a constant speed of 15 mi/hr. Draw free-body diagrams of the boat from both top and rear viewpoints, showing forces acting in all three coordinate directions. Use these diagrams to determine the *total* horizontal force on the boat in the direction tangent to its path, the *total* horizontal force on the boat in the direction perpendicular to its path and the *total* vertical force acting on the boat.

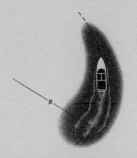

Solution

1. The boat has *negligible size* so that it can be modelled as a particle.
2. Imagine the boat to be separated or detached from the system.
3. The (detached) boat is subjected to four *external* forces.
4. Draw the free-body diagrams of the (detached) boat from both the top and rear viewpoints. Which information given in the question suggests you use a $nt-$coordinate system as the chosen inertial system?

   Show the corresponding acceleration components on a kinetic diagram or on the inertial coordinate system chosen in the free-body diagrams.

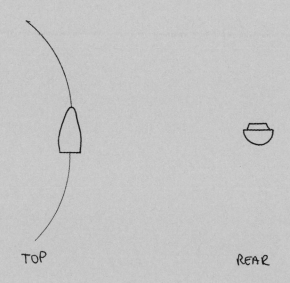

TOP   REAR

5. Using the $nt-$axes system on the free-body diagram, write down the equation of motion in the $n-$ and $t-$directions:

$$+ \leftarrow \sum F_x = ma_x :$$

$$+\uparrow \ \sum F_y = ma_y :$$

6. Write down the equation of motion in the vertical direction:

$$+\uparrow \quad \sum F_{vert} = ma_{vert} :$$

7. Solve for the required *total* forces.

Problem 3.12

The boat weighs 2600 lb with its passengers. It is moving in a circular path of radius $R = 80$ ft at a constant speed of 15 mi/hr. Draw free-body diagrams of the boat from both top and rear viewpoints, showing forces acting in all three coordinate directions. Use these diagrams to determine the *total* horizontal force on the boat in the direction tangent to its path, the *total* horizontal force on the boat in the direction perpendicular to its path and the *total* vertical force acting on the boat.

Solution

1. The boat has *negligible size* so that it can be modelled as a particle.

2. Imagine the boat to be separated or detached from the system.

3. The (detached) boat is subjected to four *external* forces.

4. Draw the free-body diagrams of the (detached) boat from both the top and rear viewpoints. Which information given in the question suggests you use a $nt-$coordinate system as the chosen inertial system?

   CURVILINEAR PATH

   Show the corresponding acceleration components on a kinetic diagram or on the inertial coordinate system chosen in the free-body diagrams.

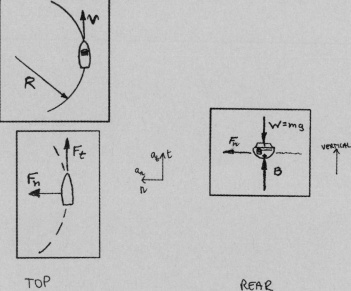

TOP   REAR

5. Using the $nt-$axes system on the free-body diagram, write down the equation of motion in the $n-$ and $t-$directions:

$$+ \leftarrow \sum F_x = ma_x : \sum F_n = \frac{mv^2}{R}$$

$$+\uparrow \; \sum F_y = ma_y : \sum F_t = m\frac{dv}{dt}$$

6. Write down the equation of motion in the vertical direction: $+\uparrow \; \sum F_{vert} = ma_{vert} : B - mg = 0$

7. Solve for the required *total* forces. Here, $\frac{dv}{dt} = 0$, $R = 80$ ft, $v = 15$ mi/hr $= 22$ ft/s. The equations of motion now give $a_t = 0$, $a_n = 6.05$ ft/s^2, $a_{vert} = 0$. Hence, the associated forces are:

$$\sum F_t = 0, \quad \sum F_n = 488.5 \text{ lb (inward, toward center of curvature), .}$$
$$\sum F_{vert} = 0.$$

Problem 3.13

Each of the blocks has mass m. The coefficient of kinetic friction at all surfaces of contact is μ_k. A horizontal force **R** is applied to the bottom block. Draw free-body diagrams for each of the top and bottom blocks.

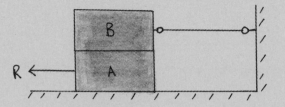

Solution

1. The size/shape of the blocks does not affect the motion under consideration. Consequently, we assume that the blocks have *negligible size* so that they can be modelled as particles.

2. Imagine each block to be separated or detached from the system (two blocks + plane).

3. The (detached) upper block is subjected to four *external* forces. They are caused by:
   The (detached) lower block is subjected to six external forces. They are caused by:

   i.   ii.

   iii.   iv.

   v.   vi.

4. Draw the free-body diagrams of each (detached) block showing all these forces labeled with their magnitudes and directions. Include any other information e.g. angles, lengths etc which may help when formulating the equations of motion.

5. Show the acceleration of block A on a kinetic diagram or on the inertial coordinate system chosen in the free-body diagram.

TOP
(B)

BOTTOM
(A)

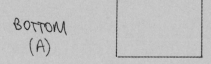

Problem 3.13

Each of the blocks has mass m. The coefficient of kinetic friction at all surfaces of contact is μ_k. A horizontal force **R** is applied to the bottom block. Draw free-body diagrams for each of the top and bottom blocks.

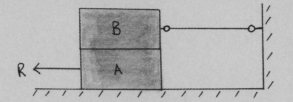

Solution

1. The size/shape of the blocks does not affect the motion under consideration. Consequently, we assume that the blocks have *negligible size* so that they can be modelled as particles.

2. Imagine each block to be separated or detached from the system (two blocks + plane).

3. The (detached) upper block is subjected to four *external* forces. They are caused by:

   i. **It's Weight**   ii. **CableTension T**

   iii. **Friction Between Blocks**   iv. **Reaction From Lower Block**

   The (detached) lower block is subjected to six external forces. They are caused by:

   i. **It's Weight**   ii. **Force P**

   iii. **Friction at Supporting Surface**   iv. **Friction with Upper Block**

   v. **Reaction From Supporting Surface**   vi. **Reaction from Upper Block**

4. Draw the free-body diagrams of each (detached) block showing all these forces labeled with their magnitudes and directions. Include any other information e.g. angles, lengths etc which may help when formulating the equations of motion.

5. Show the acceleration of block A on a kinetic diagram or on the inertial coordinate system chosen in the free-body diagram.

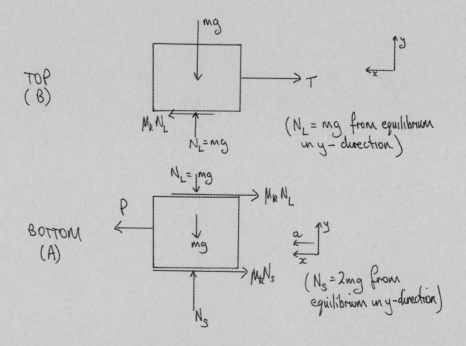

Problem 3.14

Block A has mass m_1 and block B has mass m_2. The coefficient of kinetic friction at all surfaces of contact is μ_k. Draw free-body and kinetic diagrams for each of the blocks. Explain the significance of each quantity on the free-body and kinetic diagrams.

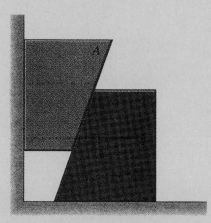

Solution

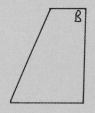

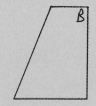

Problem 3.14

Block *A* has mass m_1 and block *B* has mass m_2. The coefficient of kinetic friction at all surfaces of contact is μ_k. Draw free-body and kinetic diagrams for each of the blocks. Explain the significance of each quantity on the free-body and kinetic diagrams.

Solution

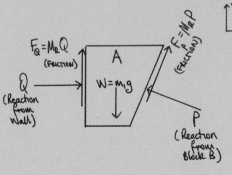

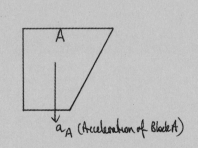

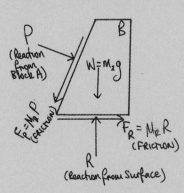

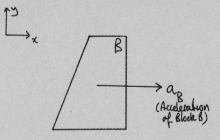

Problem 3.15

Block A has mass m_1 and block B has mass m_2. The coefficient of kinetic friction at all surfaces of contact is μ_k. Draw free-body and kinetic diagrams for each of the blocks (assume that sliding has begun). Explain the significance of each quantity on the free-body and kinetic diagrams.

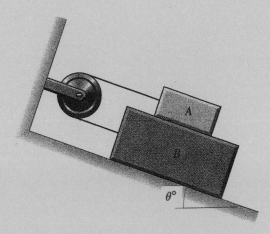

Solution

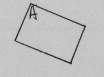

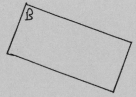

Problem 3.15

Block A has mass m_1 and block B has mass m_2. The coefficient of kinetic friction at all surfaces of contact is μ_k. Draw free-body and kinetic diagrams for each of the blocks (assume that sliding has begun). Explain the significance of each quantity on the free-body and kinetic diagrams.

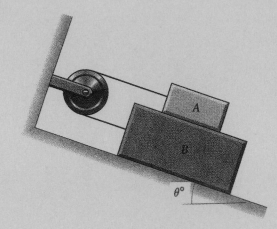

Solution

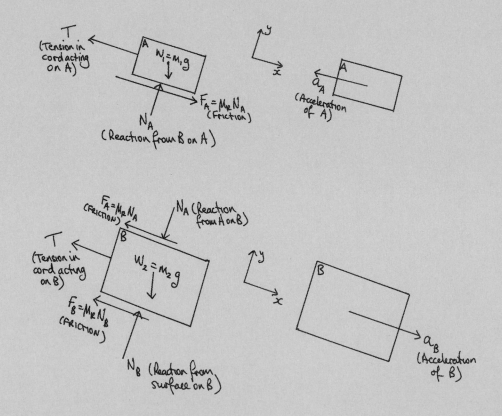

3.2 Free-Body Diagrams in Rigid Body Kinetics

Problem 3.16

The refrigerator of mass m rests on casters at A and B. Suppose that you push on it with a horizontal force of magnitude F as shown and that the casters remain on the floor. Draw the free-body and kinetic diagrams of the refrigerator. Neglect the mass of the casters.

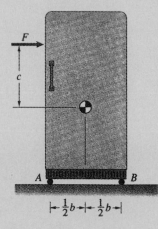

Solution

1. Imagine the refrigerator to be separated or detached from the system (refrigerator + floor).
2. The refrigerator is subjected to four *external* forces. They are caused by:

   i.   **ii.**

   iii.   **iv.**

3. Draw the free-body diagram of the (detached) refrigerator showing all these forces labeled with their magnitudes and directions. Include any other relevant information e.g. lengths, angles etc which may help when formulating the equations of motion (including the moment equation) for the refrigerator.
4. Draw the corresponding kinetic diagram.

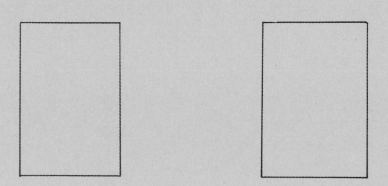

Problem 3.16

The refrigerator of mass m rests on casters at A and B. Suppose that you push on it with a horizontal force of magnitude F as shown and that the casters remain on the floor. Draw the free-body and kinetic diagrams of the refrigerator. Neglect the mass of the casters.

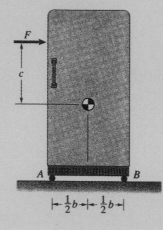

Solution

1. Imagine the refrigerator to be separated or detached from the system (refrigerator + floor).
2. The refrigerator is subjected to four *external* forces. They are caused by:

   i. Force F   **ii. Weight**

   iii. Reaction at A   **iv. Reaction at B**

3. Draw the free-body diagram of the (detached) refrigerator showing all these forces labeled with their magnitudes and directions. Include any other relevant information e.g. lengths, angles etc which may help when formulating the equations of motion (including the moment equation) for the refrigerator.
4. Draw the corresponding kinetic diagram.

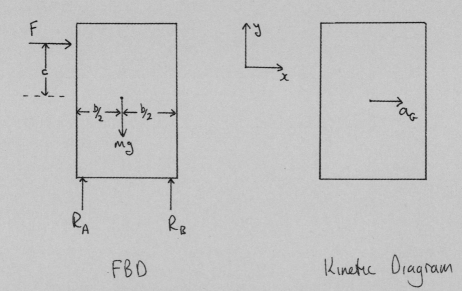

Problem 3.17

The 14000 lb airplane's arresting hook exerts the force of magnitude F and causes the plane to decelerate at $6g$. Draw the free-body and kinetic diagrams of the airplane. Neglect the mass of the wheels.

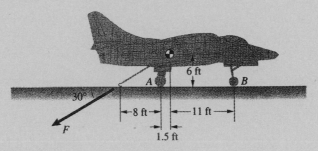

Solution

1. Imagine the airplane to be separated or detached from the system (airplane + ground).
2. The airplane is subjected to six *external* forces. They are caused by:

    i.   ii.

    iii.   iv.

    v.   vi.

3. Draw the free-body diagram of the (detached) airplane showing all these forces labeled with their magnitudes and directions. Include any other relevant information e.g. lengths, angles etc which may help when formulating the equations of motion (including the moment equation) for the airplane.
4. Draw the corresponding kinetic diagram.

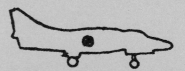

Problem 3.17

The 14000 lb airplane's arresting hook exerts the force of magnitude F and causes the plane to decelerate at $6g$. Draw the free-body and kinetic diagrams of the airplane. Neglect the mass of the wheels.

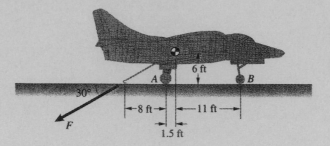

Solution

1. Imagine the airplane to be separated or detached from the system (airplane + ground).
2. The airplane is subjected to six *external* forces. They are caused by:

   i. **Weight**   ii. **Force F**

   iii. **Reaction at** A iv. **Reaction at** B

   v. **Friction at** A vi. **Friction at** B

3. Draw the free-body diagram of the (detached) airplane showing all these forces labeled with their magnitudes and directions. Include any other relevant information e.g. lengths, angles etc which may help when formulating the equations of motion (including the moment equation) for the airplane.
4. Draw the corresponding kinetic diagram.

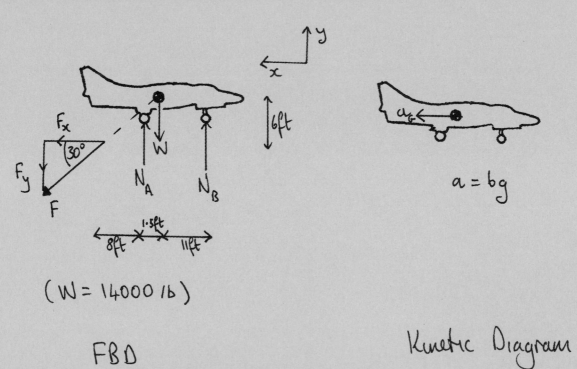

Problem 3.18

A student catching a ride to his summer job unwisely supports himself in the back of an accelerating truck by exerting a horizontal force of magnitude F_H on the truck's cab at A. Draw the free-body and kinetic diagrams of the student.

Solution

1. Imagine the student to be separated or detached from the system.
2. The student is subjected to four *external* forces. They are caused by:

   i.   ii.

   iii.   iv.

3. Draw the free-body diagram of the (detached) student showing all these forces labeled with their magnitudes and directions. Include any other relevant information e.g. lengths, angles etc which may help when formulating the equations of motion (including the moment equation) for the student.
4. Draw the corresponding kinetic diagram.

Problem 3.18

A student catching a ride to his summer job unwisely supports himself in the back of an accelerating truck by exerting a horizontal force of magnitude F_H on the truck's cab at A. Draw the free-body and kinetic diagrams of the student.

Solution

1. Imagine the student to be separated or detached from the system.

2. The student is subjected to four *external* forces. They are caused by:

   i. **His weight**

   ii. **Normal force on his feet**

   iii. **Friction on his feet**

   iv. **Force F_H exerted on student by truck**

3. Draw the free-body diagram of the (detached) student showing all these forces labeled with their magnitudes and directions. Include any other relevant information e.g. lengths, angles etc which may help when formulating the equations of motion (including the moment equation) for the student.

4. Draw the corresponding kinetic diagram.

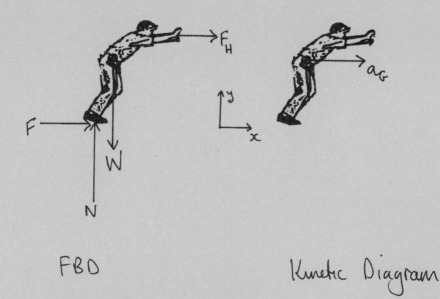

Problem 3.19

The combined mass of the person and bicycle is m. The location of their combined center of mass is as shown. Draw the free-body and kinetic diagrams of the combined person and bicycle.

Solution

1. Imagine the combined person and bicycle to be separated or detached from the system.
2. The combined person and bicycle is subjected to five *external* forces. They are caused by:

   i.   ii.

   iii.   iv.

   v.

3. Draw the free-body diagram of the (detached) combined person and bicycle showing all these forces labeled with their magnitudes and directions. Include any other relevant information e.g. lengths, angles etc which may help when formulating the equations of motion (including the moment equation) for the pipe.
4. Draw the corresponding kinetic diagram.

Problem 3.19

The combined mass of the person and bicycle is m. The location of their combined center of mass is as shown. Draw the free-body and kinetic diagrams of the combined person and bicycle.

Solution

1. Imagine the combined person and bicycle to be separated or detached from the system.
2. The combined person and bicycle is subjected to five *external* forces. They are caused by:

    i. Weight   **ii. Reaction at A**

    iii. Reaction at B   **iv. Friction at A**

    v. Friction at B

3. Draw the free-body diagram of the (detached) combined person and bicycle showing all these forces labeled with their magnitudes and directions. Include any other relevant information e.g. lengths, angles etc which may help when formulating the equations of motion (including the moment equation) for the pipe.
4. Draw the corresponding kinetic diagram.

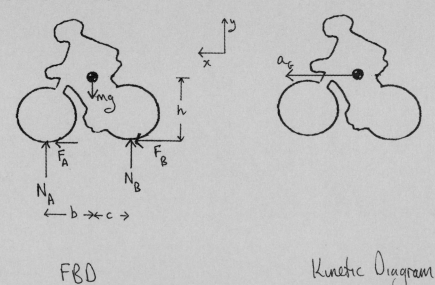

FBD   Kinetic Diagram

Problem 3.20

The slender bar has mass m and is released from rest in the horizontal position. Draw the free-body and kinetic diagrams of the bar at that instant.

Solution

1. Imagine the bar to be separated or detached from the system.
2. The desk is subjected to three *external* forces. They are caused by:

   i.   **ii.**

   iii.

3. Draw the free-body diagram of the (detached) bar showing all these forces labeled with their magnitudes and directions. Include any other relevant information e.g. lengths, angles etc which may help when formulating the equations of motion (including the moment equation) for the bar.
4. Draw the corresponding kinetic diagram for the bar at the instant in question.

Problem 3.20

The slender bar has mass m and is released from rest in the horizontal position. Draw the free-body and kinetic diagrams of the bar at that instant.

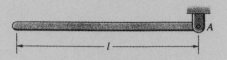

Solution

1. Imagine the bar to be separated or detached from the system.
2. The desk is subjected to three *external* forces. They are caused by:
   - i. **(2) Reactions at the pin support**   ii.
   - iii. **Weight of bar**
3. Draw the free-body diagram of the (detached) bar showing all these forces labeled with their magnitudes and directions. Include any other relevant information e.g. lengths, angles etc which may help when formulating the equations of motion (including the moment equation) for the bar.
4. Draw the corresponding kinetic diagram for the bar at the instant in question.

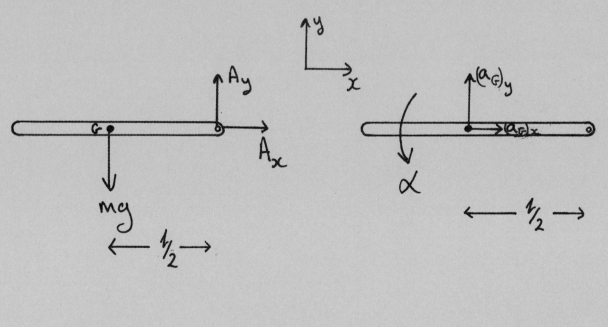

Problem 3.21

The gears A and B can turn freely on their pin supports in the vertical plane. Their masses and moments of inertia are m_A, m_B, I_A and I_B, respectively. They are initially stationary and , at $t = 0$, a constant couple of magnitude M is applied to gear B. Draw free-body and kinetic diagrams for each of the gears at this instant.

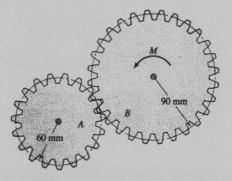

Solution

1. Imagine each gear to be separated or detached from the system.
2. Gear B is subjected to four *external* forces and one couple moment. They are caused by:

   i.   ii.

   iii.   iv.

   v.

   Gear A is subjected to four *external* forces. They are caused by:

   i.   ii.

   iii.   iv.

3. Draw the free-body diagram of each (detached) gear showing all these forces labeled with their magnitudes and directions. Include any other relevant information e.g. lengths, angles etc which may help when formulating the equations of motion (including the moment equation) for the gears.
4. Draw the corresponding kinetic diagrams for each gear.

Problem 3.21

The gears A and B can turn freely on their pin supports in the vertical plane. Their masses and moments of inertia are m_A, m_B, I_A and I_B, respectively. They are initially stationary and , at $t = 0$, a constant couple of magnitude M is applied to gear B. Draw free-body and kinetic diagrams for each of the gears at this instant.

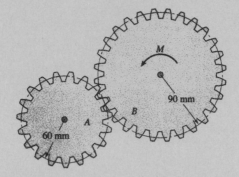

Solution

1. Imagine each gear to be separated or detached from the system.

2. Gear B is subjected to four *external* forces and one couple moment. They are caused by:

   i. Weight   **ii. (2) Pin reactions**

   iii. Friction at contact with gear A   **iv. Couple of magnitude M**

   Gear A is subjected to four *external* forces. They are caused by:

   i. Weight   **ii. (2) Pin reactions**

   iii. Friction at contact with gear B

3. Draw the free-body diagram of each (detached) gear showing all these forces labeled with their magnitudes and directions. Include any other relevant information e.g. lengths, angles etc which may help when formulating the equations of motion (including the moment equation) for the gears.

4. Draw the corresponding kinetic diagrams for each gear.

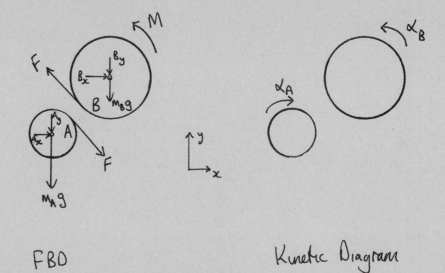

FBD   Kinetic Diagram

Problem 3.22

The moment of inertia of the pulley is I_P slug-ft^2. Draw separate free-body and kinetic diagrams for the pulley and the 20 lb weight.

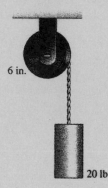

6 in.

20 lb

Solution

1. Imagine first the pulley then the weight to be separated or detached from the system.

2. The pulley is subjected to four *external* forces. They are caused by:

    i.   ii.

    iii.   iv.

    The weight is subjected to two *external* forces. They are caused by:

    i.   ii.

3. Draw the free-body diagram of each of the (detached) pulley and weight showing all these forces labeled with their magnitudes and directions. Include any other relevant information e.g. lengths, angles etc which may help when formulating the equations of motion (including the moment equation) for the weight and/or pulley.

4. Draw the corresponding kinetic diagrams for each of the weight and pulley.

Problem 3.22

The moment of inertia of the pulley is I_P slug-ft^2. Draw separate free-body and kinetic diagrams for the pulley and the 20 lb weight.

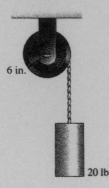

6 in.

20 lb

Solution

1. Imagine first the pulley then the weight to be separated or detached from the system.
2. The pulley is subjected to four *external* forces. They are caused by:
   - **i. Weight**   **ii. (2) Pin reactions**
   - **iii. Tension in rope**

   The weight is subjected to two *external* forces. They are caused by:
   - **i. Weight**   **ii. Tension in rope**
3. Draw the free-body diagram of each of the (detached) pulley and weight showing all these forces labeled with their magnitudes and directions. Include any other relevant information e.g. lengths, angles etc which may help when formulating the equations of motion (including the moment equation) for the weight and/or pulley.
4. Draw the corresponding kinetic diagrams for each of the weight and pulley.

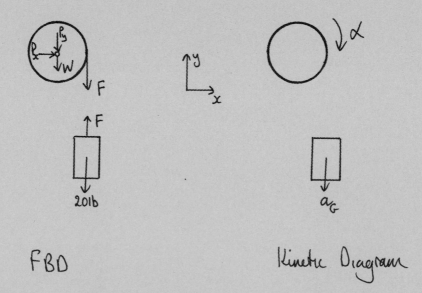

FBD   Kinetic Diagram

Problem 3.23

Box A has mass m_A, box B has mass m_B and the pulley has mass m_P. If the boxes start from rest at $t = 0$, draw free-body diagrams for each of the boxes and the pulley as box B slides down the slope. The coefficient of kinetic friction between the surface and the boxes is μ_k.

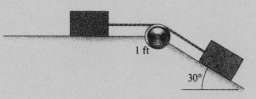

Solution

1. Imagine each box and the pulley to be separated or detached from the system.
2. Each box is subjected to four *external* forces. They are caused by:

   i.   **ii.**

   iii.   **iv.**

   The pulley is subjected to five *external* forces. They are caused by:

   i.   **ii.**

   iii.   **iv.**

   v.

3. Draw the free-body diagrams of the (detached) boxes and pulley showing all these forces labeled with their magnitudes and directions. Include any other relevant information e.g. lengths, angles etc which may help when formulating the equations of motion (including the moment equation) for the boxes and/or the pulley.
4. Include any useful kinetic information on the free-body diagrams.

Problem 3.23

Box A has mass m_A, box B has mass m_B and the pulley has mass m_P. If the boxes start from rest at $t = 0$, draw free-body diagrams for each of the boxes and the pulley as box B slides down the slope. The coefficient of kinetic friction between the surface and the boxes is μ_k.

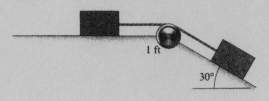

1 ft

30°

Solution

1. Imagine each box and the pulley to be separated or detached from the system.
2. Each box is subjected to four *external* forces. They are caused by:

   i. **Weight**   ii. **Reaction at surface**

   iii. **Friction at surface**   iv. **Tension in rope**

   The pulley is subjected to five *external* forces. They are caused by:

   i. **Weight**   ii. **(2) pin reactions**

   iii. **Tension in lower rope**   iv. **Tension in upper rope**

3. Draw the free-body diagrams of the (detached) boxes and pulley showing all these forces labeled with their magnitudes and directions. Include any other relevant information e.g. lengths, angles etc which may help when formulating the equations of motion (including the moment equation) for the boxes and/or the pulley.
4. Include any useful kinetic information on the free-body diagrams.

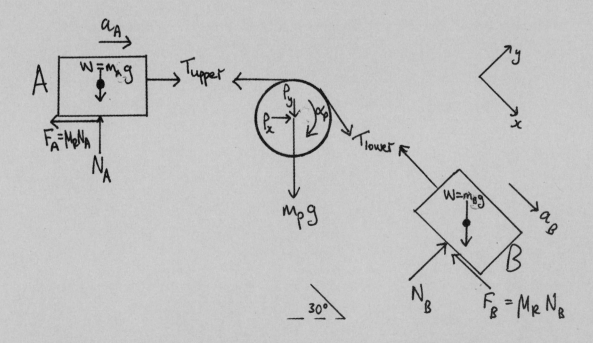

Problem 3.24

The slender bar weighs 10 lb and the disk weighs 20 lb. The coefficient of kinetic friction between the disk and the horizontal surface is μ_k. The disk has an initial counterclockwise angular velocity ω. Draw the free-body diagrams of the bar and the disk as the disk slides.

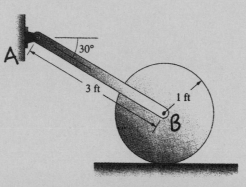

Solution

1. Imagine the disk and the bar each to be separated or detached from the system.

2. The disk is subjected to five *external* forces. They are caused by:

   i.   ii.

   iii.   iv.

   v.

   The bar is subjected to five *external* forces. They are caused by:

   i.   ii.

   iii.   iv.

   v.

3. Draw the free-body diagrams of the (detached) bar and disk showing all these forces labeled with their magnitudes and directions. Include any other relevant information e.g. lengths, angles etc which may help when formulating the equations of motion (including the moment equation) for the disk.

4. On the free-body diagrams, indicate clearly the acceleration components of the bar and disk.

Problem 3.24

The slender bar weighs 10 lb and the disk weighs 20 lb. The coefficient of kinetic friction between the disk and the horizontal surface is μ_k. The disk has an initial counterclockwise angular velocity ω. Draw the free-body diagrams of the bar and the disk as the disk slides.

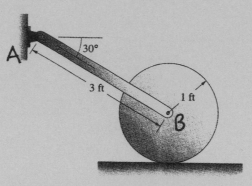

Solution

1. Imagine the disk and the bar each to be separated or detached from the system.
2. The disk is subjected to five *external* forces. They are caused by:

    i. **Weight**   ii. **(2) pin reactions at** B

    iii. **Reaction at surface**   iv. **Friction at surface**

    The bar is subjected to five *external* forces. They are caused by:

    i. **Weight**   ii. **(2) pin reactions at** A

    iii. **(2) pin reactions at** B

3. Draw the free-body diagrams of the (detached) bar and disk showing all these forces labeled with their magnitudes and directions. Include any other relevant information e.g. lengths, angles etc which may help when formulating the equations of motion (including the moment equation) for the disk.
4. On the free-body diagrams, indicate clearly the acceleration components of the bar and disk.

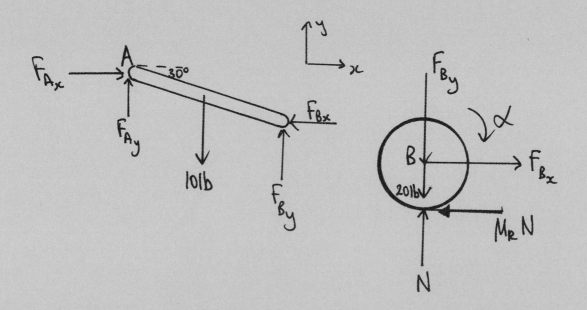

Problem 3.25

The object consists of identical 1–m, 5–kg bars welded together. If it is released from rest in the position shown, draw free-body and kinetic diagrams of the object at that instant. The center of mass of the system is shown.

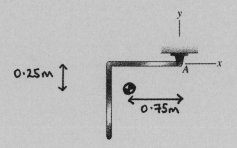

Solution

1. Imagine the object to be separated or detached from the pin at A.
2. The object is subjected to three *external* forces. They are caused by:

    i.   **ii.**

   iii.

3. Draw the free-body diagram of the (detached) object showing all these forces labeled with their magnitudes and directions. Include any other relevant information e.g. lengths, angles etc which may help when formulating the equations of motion (including the moment equation) for the object.
4. Draw the corresponding kinetic diagram indicating clearly the acceleration components of the object.

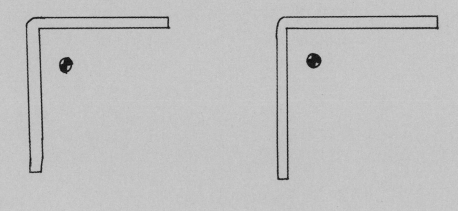

Problem 3.25

The object consists of identical 1−m, 5−kg bars welded together. If it is released from rest in the position shown, draw free-body and kinetic diagrams of the object at that instant. The center of mass of the system is shown.

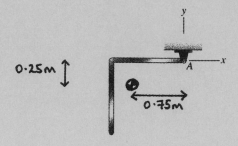

Solution

1. Imagine the object to be separated or detached from the pin at A.
2. The object is subjected to three *external* forces. They are caused by:

   i. Weight   **ii. (2)pin reactions at A**

3. Draw the free-body diagram of the (detached) object showing all these forces labeled with their magnitudes and directions. Include any other relevant information e.g. lengths, angles etc which may help when formulating the equations of motion (including the moment equation) for the object.
4. Draw the corresponding kinetic diagram indicating clearly the acceleration components of the object.

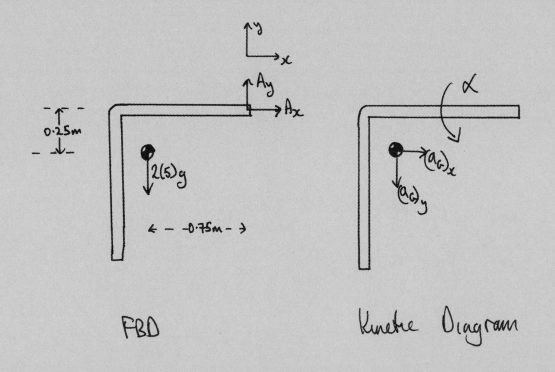

Problem 3.26

Model the arm ABC as a single rigid body. Its mass is 300 kg and the moment of inertia about its center of mass is I. If point A is stationary and the angular acceleration of the arm is α_{arm}, counterclockwise, draw a free-body diagram for the arm ABC.

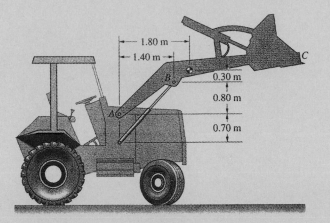

Solution

1. Imagine the arm ABC to be separated or detached from the system.
2. The arm is subjected to four *external* forces They are caused by:

   i.   ii.

   iii.   iv.

3. Draw the free-body diagram of the (detached) arm showing all these forces labeled with their magnitudes and directions. Include any other relevant information e.g. lengths, angles etc which may help when formulating the equations of motion (including the moment equation) for the arm.
4. Indicate the acceleration components of the arm on the coordinate axes system chosen in the free-body diagram.

Problem 3.26

Model the arm ABC as a single rigid body. Its mass is 300 kg and the moment of inertia about its center of mass is I. If point A is stationary and the angular acceleration of the arm is α_{arm}, counterclockwise, draw a free-body diagram for the arm ABC.

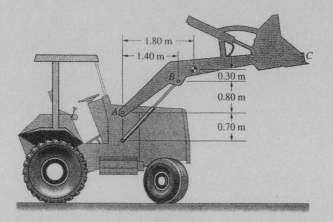

Solution

1. Imagine the arm ABC to be separated or detached from the system.
2. The arm is subjected to four *external* forces They are caused by:

   i. **Weight**   ii. **(2) pin reactions at A**

   iii. **Force exerted by hydraulic cylinder at B**

3. Draw the free-body diagram of the (detached) arm showing all these forces labeled with their magnitudes and directions. Include any other relevant information e.g. lengths, angles etc which may help when formulating the equations of motion (including the moment equation) for the arm.
4. Indicate the acceleration components of the arm on the coordinate axes system chosen in the free-body diagram.

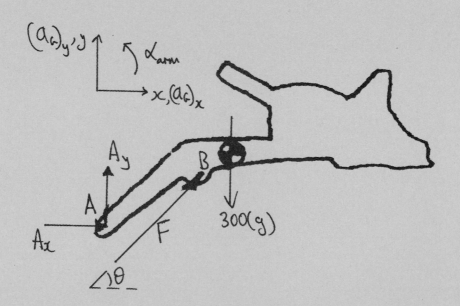

Problem 3.27

Arm BC has a mass of 12 kg and the moment of inertia about its center of mass is 3 kg-m^2. If B is stationary (fixed support) and arm BC has a constant counterclockwise angular velocity of 2 rad/s at the instant shown, use a free-body diagram of arm BC to determine the couple and the components of force exerted on arm BC at B.

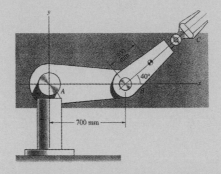

Solution

1. Imagine the arm to be separated or detached from the system.

2. The arm is subjected to three *external* forces and one external couple. They are caused by:

   i. _____   **ii.** _____

   iii. _____   **iv.** _____

    v. _____   **vi.** _____

3. Draw the free-body diagram of the (detached) arm showing all these forces labeled with their magnitudes and directions. Include any other relevant information e.g. lengths, angles etc which may help when formulating the equations of motion (including the moment equation) for the arm.

4. Indicate the acceleration components of the arm on the coordinate axes system chosen in the free-body diagram.

5. Sum moments about the fixed point B (the arm is in rotation about B) and write down the moment equation of motion:

$$\circlearrowleft + \sum M_B = I_B \alpha :$$

6. Solve for the couple exerted at B.

7. Write down equations of motion in each of the $x-$ (horizontal) and $y-$ (vertical) directions:

$$+\rightarrow \sum F_x = m\,(a_G)_x :$$

$$+\uparrow \;\; \sum F_y = m\,(a_G)_y :$$

8. Use kinematics to determine the components $(a_G)_x$ and $(a_G)_y$:

9. Solve the equations of motion in the x and y directions to determine the reactions at B:

Problem 3.27

Arm BC has a mass of 12 kg and the moment of inertia about its center of mass is 3 kg-m^2. If B is stationary (fixed support) and arm BC has a constant counterclockwise angular velocity of 2 rad/s at the instant shown, use a free-body diagram of arm BC to determine the couple and the components of force exerted on arm BC at B.

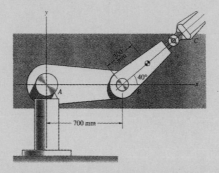

Solution

1. Imagine the arm to be separated or detached from the system.

2. The arm is subjected to three *external* forces and one external couple.
   They are caused by:

   i. (1) couple and (2) force reactions at B   **ii. Weight**

3. Draw the free-body diagram of the (detached) arm showing all these forces labeled with their magnitudes and directions. Include any other relevant information e.g. lengths, angles etc. which may help when formulating the equations of motion (including the moment equation) for the arm.

4. Indicate the acceleration components of the arm on the coordinate axes system chosen in the free-body diagram.

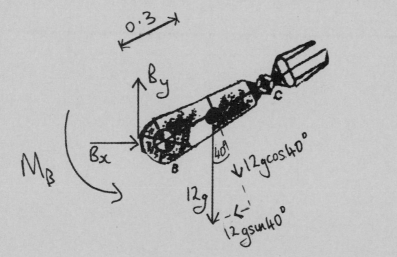
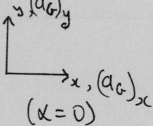

5. Sum moments about the fixed point B (the arm is in rotation about B) and write down the moment equation of motion:
   $$\circlearrowleft + \sum M_B = I_B \alpha : M_B - 0.3 \cos 40°(12)(9.81) = I_B(0)$$

6. Solve for the couple exerted at B. $\mathbf{M}_B = 27.05\,\mathbf{k}$.

7. Write down equations of motion in each of the $x-$ (horizontal) and $y-$ (vertical) directions:
   $$+\rightarrow \sum F_x = m(a_G)_x : B_x = m(a_G)_x = 12(a_G)_x$$

   $$+\uparrow \sum F_y = m(a_G)_y : B_y - mg = m(a_G)_y \Leftrightarrow B_y - 12g = 12(a_G)_y$$

8. Use kinematics to determine the components $(a_G)_x$ and $(a_G)_y$:

$$a = (a_G)_x \mathbf{i} + (a_G)_x \mathbf{j}$$
$$= \boldsymbol{\alpha} \times \mathbf{r}_{CM/O} - \omega^2 \mathbf{r}_{CM/O}$$
$$= -(2)^2 (0.3 \cos 40° \mathbf{i} + 0.3 \sin 40° \mathbf{j}$$
$$= -0.919\mathbf{i} - 0.771\mathbf{j} (m/s^2)$$

$$(a_G)_x = -0.919, \quad (a_G)_y = -0.771$$

9. Solve the equations of motion in the x and y directions to determine the reactions at B:

$$Bx = -11.03 \ N, \ By = 108.5 \ N.$$

Problem 3.28

A circular disk of mass m and radius R is released from rest on an inclined surface and allowed to roll a distance D. Draw free-body and kinetic diagrams for the disk as it rolls.

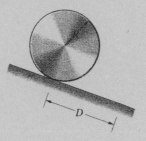

Solution

1. Imagine the disk to be separated or detached from the system.
2. The disk is subjected to three *external* forces. They are caused by:

   i.   ii.

   iii.

3. Draw the free-body diagram of the (detached) disk showing all these forces labeled with their magnitudes and directions. Include any other relevant information e.g. lengths, angles etc which may help when formulating the equations of motion (including the moment equation) for the disk.
4. Indicate the acceleration components of the disk on the corresponding kinetic diagram.

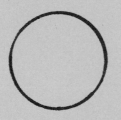

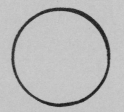

Problem 3.28

A circular disk of mass m and radius R is released from rest on an inclined surface and allowed to roll a distance D. Draw free-body and kinetic diagrams for the disk as it rolls.

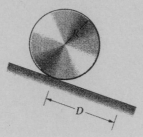

Solution

1. Imagine the disk to be separated or detached from the system.
2. The disk is subjected to three external forces. They are caused by:

   i. **Weight**   ii. **Normal reaction at surface**

   iii. **Friction at surface**

3. Draw the free-body diagram of the (detached) disk showing all these forces labeled with their magnitudes and directions. Include any other relevant information e.g. lengths, angles etc which may help when formulating the equations of motion (including the moment equation) for the disk.
4. Indicate the acceleration components of the disk on the corresponding kinetic diagram.

F

$\downarrow mg$

N θ

FBD

α

$(a_G)_x = a_G$

Kinetic Diagram

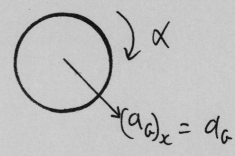

Problem 3.29

The homogeneous disk weighs 100 lb and its radius is $R = 1$ ft. It rolls on the plane surface. The spring constant is $k = 100$ lb/ft. If the disk is rolled to the left until the spring is compressed 1 ft and released from rest, use a free-body diagram of the disk to determine the disk's angular acceleration at the instant the disk is released.

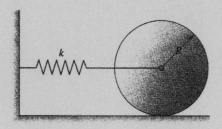

Solution

1. Imagine the disk to be separated or detached from the system.
2. The spool is subjected to four *external* forces. They are caused by:

   i.   ii.

   iii.   iv.

3. Draw the free-body diagram of the (detached) disk showing all these forces labeled with their magnitudes and directions. Include any other relevant information e.g. lengths, angles etc which may help when formulating the equations of motion (including the moment equation) for the spool.

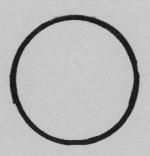

4. Sum moments about the center of the disk and write down the moment equation of motion: $\circlearrowright + \sum M_G = I_G \alpha$:
5. Write down equations of motion in each of the $x-$ (horizontal) and $y-$ (vertical) directions:

   $+\rightarrow \sum F_x = m\,(a_G)_x$:

   $+\uparrow \ \sum F_y = m\,(a_G)_y$:
6. Solve for the required angular acceleration α.

Problem 3.29

The homogeneous disk weighs 100 lb and its radius is $R = 1$ ft. It rolls on the plane surface. The spring constant is $k = 100$ lb/ft. If the disk is rolled to the left until the spring is compressed 1 ft and released from rest, use a free-body diagram of the disk to determine the disk's angular acceleration at the instant the disk is released.

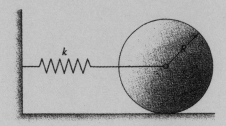

Solution

1. Imagine the disk to be separated or detached from the system.
2. The spool is subjected to four external forces. They are caused by:

   i. Weight   **ii.** Spring force

   iii. Normal reaction at surface   **iv.** Friction at surface

3. Draw the free-body diagram of the (detached) disk showing all these forces labeled with their magnitudes and directions. Include any other relevant information e.g. lengths, angles etc which may help when formulating the equations of motion (including the moment equation) for the spool.

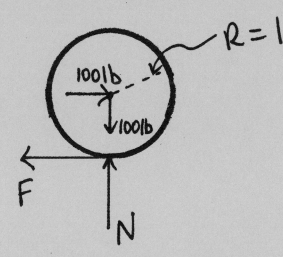
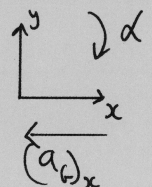

4. Sum moments about the center of the disk and write down the moment equation of motion:
   $$\circlearrowleft + \sum M_G = I_G \alpha : -(1)(F) = I_G \alpha = \tfrac{1}{2} m (1)^2 \alpha = \tfrac{1}{2} \left(\tfrac{100}{32.2} \right) (1)^2 \alpha$$
5. Write down equations of motion in each of the $x-$ (horizontal) and $y-$ (vertical) directions:
   $$+\rightarrow \sum Fx = m (a_G) x : 100 - F = m (a_G) x = \left(\tfrac{100}{32.2} \right) (1) \alpha \text{ (disk rolls)}$$

   $$+\uparrow \ \sum Fy = m (a_G) y : N - 100 = 0$$
6. Solve for the required angular acceleration α. $\alpha = -21.5 \ \mathbf{k}$

Problem 3.30

The ring gear is fixed. The mass and moment of inertia of the sun gear are m_s and I_s, respectively. The mass and moment of inertia of each planet gear are m_p and I_p, respectively. If a couple of magnitude M is applied to the sun gear, draw free-body and kinetic diagrams for the sun gear and planet gear A.

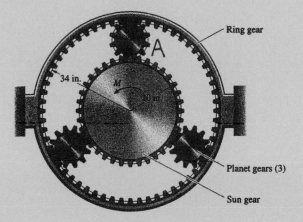

Solution

1. Imagine each of the sun and planet gear to be separated or detached from the system.
2. The sun gear is subjected to seven *external* forces and one external couple. The planet gear is subjected to five external forces.
3. Draw the free-body diagrams of the (detached) sun and planet gears showing all these forces labeled with their magnitudes and directions. Include any other relevant information e.g. lengths, angles etc which may help when formulating the equations of motion (including the moment equation) for the gears.
4. Draw the corresponding kinetic diagrams indicating clearly the acceleration components of each gear.

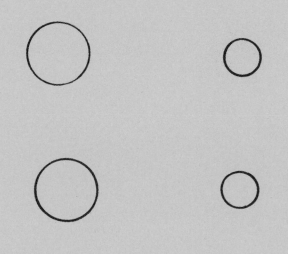

Problem 3.30

The ring gear is fixed. The mass and moment of inertia of the sun gear are m_s and I_s, respectively. The mass and moment of inertia of each planet gear are m_p and I_p, respectively. If a couple of magnitude M is applied to the sun gear, draw free-body and kinetic diagrams for the sun gear and planet gear A.

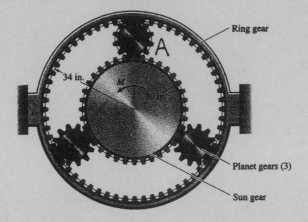

Solution

1. Imagine each of the sun and planet gear to be separated or detached from the system.
2. The sun gear is subjected to seven external forces and one external couple. The planet gear is subjected to five external forces.
3. Draw the free-body diagrams of the (detached) sun and planet gears showing all these forces labeled with their magnitudes and directions. Include any other relevant information e.g. lengths, angles etc which may help when formulating the equations of motion (including the moment equation) for the gears.
4. Draw the corresponding kinetic diagrams indicating clearly the acceleration components of each gear.

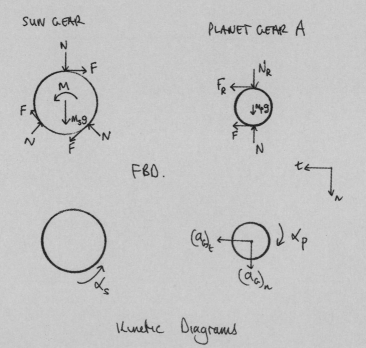

Problem 3.31

The 18 kg ladder is released from rest in the position shown. Model the ladder as a slender bar. Draw the free-body and kinetic diagrams for the ladder as end B slides to the right. The coefficient of kinetic friction between the ladder and all surfaces is μ_k.

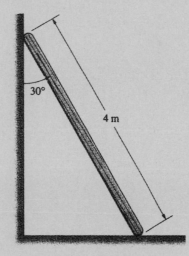

Solution

1. Imagine the ladder to be separated or detached from the system.
2. The ladder is subjected to five *external* forces.
3. Draw the free-body diagram of the (detached) ladder showing all these forces labeled with their magnitudes and directions. Include any other relevant information e.g. lengths, angles etc which may help when formulating the equations of motion (including the moment equation) for the ladder.
4. Draw the corresponding kinetic diagram. Be sure to indicate the components of the vectors a_G and α.

Problem 3.31

The 18 kg ladder is released from rest in the position shown. Model the ladder as a slender bar. Draw the free-body and kinetic diagrams for the ladder as end B slides to the right. The coefficient of kinetic friction between the ladder and all surfaces is μ_k.

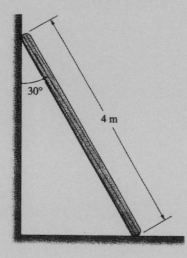

Solution

1. Imagine the ladder to be separated or detached from the system.
2. The ladder is subjected to five external forces.
3. Draw the free-body diagram of the (detached) ladder showing all these forces labeled with their magnitudes and directions. Include any other relevant information e.g. lengths, angles etc which may help when formulating the equations of motion (including the moment equation) for the ladder.
4. Draw the corresponding kinetic diagram. Be sure to indicate the components of the vectors a_G and α.

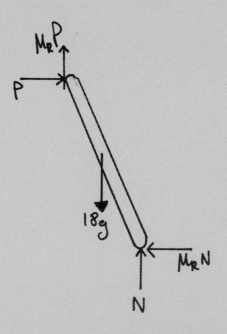

Problem 3.32

The 0.1 kg slender bar and 0.2 kg cylindrical disk are released from rest with the bar horizontal. The disk rolls on the curved surface. Draw free-body and kinetic diagrams for each of the bar and disk at that instant.

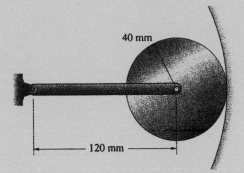

Solution

1. Imagine each of the bar and the disk to be separated or detached.
2. The detached bar is subjected to five *external* forces. The detached disk is subjected to five *external* forces.
3. Draw the free-body diagram of the (detached) bar and then the (detached) disk showing all these forces labeled with their magnitudes and directions. Include any other relevant information e.g. lengths, angles etc which may help when formulating the corresponding equations of motion.
4. Draw the corresponding kinetic diagrams indicating clearly the components of the vectors a_G and α in each case, as appropriate.

Problem 3.32

The 0.1 kg slender bar and 0.2 kg cylindrical disk are released from rest with the bar horizontal. The disk rolls on the curved surface. Draw free-body and kinetic diagrams for each of the bar and disk at that instant.

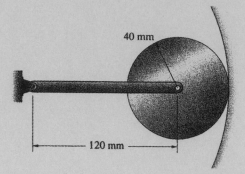

40 mm

120 mm

Solution

1. Imagine each of the bar and the disk to be separated or detached.
2. The detached bar is subjected to five external forces. The detached disk is subjected to five external forces.
3. Draw the free-body diagram of the (detached) bar and then the (detached) disk showing all these forces labeled with their magnitudes and directions. Include any other relevant information e.g. lengths, angles etc which may help when formulating the corresponding equations of motion.
4. Draw the corresponding kinetic diagrams indicating clearly the components of the vectors a_G and α in each case, as appropriate.

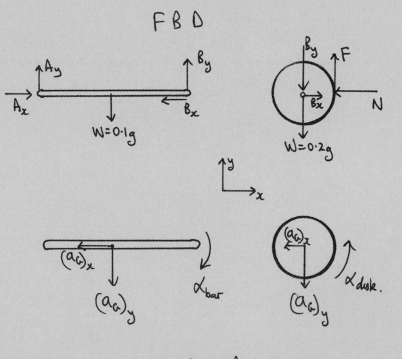

Problem 3.33

The suspended objects A and B weigh 20 lb and 40 lb, respectively. The left pulley weighs 16 lb and its moment of inertia is 0.24 slug-ft^2. The right pulley weighs 6 lb and its moment of inertia is 0.04 slug-ft^2. The system is released from rest. Draw free-body and kinetic diagrams for:

(a) The (detached) combination of left pulley with weight A attached.

(b) The right pulley detached from weight B but connected to its support.

(c) Weight B

Use these diagrams to find the acceleration of B when the system is released from rest.

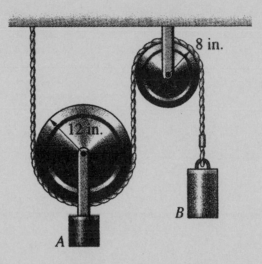

Solution

1. Imagine the combination of left pulley with attached weight A to be separated or detached from the system.

2. This combination is subjected to four *external* forces.

3. The right pulley is detached from weight B but still connected to its support. Hence, it is subjected to three external forces.

4. The (detached) weight B is subjected to two external forces.

5. When the system is released from rest: the left pulley is subjected to a counterclockwise angular acceleration and moves as if it was *rolling* on a plane surface coincident with the left part of the rope - so its center moves in a straight vertical line with upward acceleration; the right pulley is subjected to a clockwise angular acceleration and object B accelerates downward.

6. Draw the free-body diagrams in each case showing all these forces labeled with their magnitudes and directions. Include any other relevant information e.g. lengths, angles etc which may help when formulating the equations of motion (including the moment equation). Draw also the corresponding kinetic diagrams.

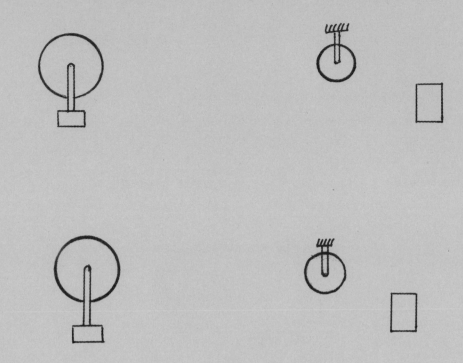

7. Write down the equation of motion in the $y-$ (vertical) direction for the weight B:

$+\uparrow \quad \sum F_y = ma_B :$

8. Sum moments about the center of the right pulley and write down the moment equation of motion:

$\circlearrowright + \sum M_G = I_G\alpha_B :$

9. For the combination of left pulley and weight A, write down the equation of motion in the $y-$ (vertical) direction:

$+\uparrow \quad \sum F_y = ma_A :$

and the moment equation about the center of the left pulley:

$\circlearrowright + \sum M_G = I_G\alpha_A :$

10. You should now have 4 equations but 7 unknowns. Notice however that:

$$a_A = r_A\alpha_A = \frac{12}{12}\alpha_A,$$

$$a_B = r_B\alpha_B = \frac{8}{12}\alpha_B,$$

$$a_B = a_A + \alpha_A \times \mathbf{r}_{B/A} - \omega_A^2\mathbf{r}_{B/A}.$$

The final equation leads to $a_B = 2\left(\frac{12}{12}\right)\alpha_A$

11. Solve the 7 equations in 7 unknowns for the required acceleration α_B:

Problem 3.33

The suspended objects A and B weigh 20 lb and 40 lb, respectively. The left pulley weighs 16 lb and its moment of inertia is 0.24 slug-ft^2. The right pulley weighs 6 lb and its moment of inertia is 0.04 slug-ft^2. The system is released from rest. Draw free-body and kinetic diagrams for:

(a) The (detached) combination of left pulley with weight A attached.

(b) The right pulley detached from weight B but connected to its support.

(c) Weight B

Use these diagrams to find the acceleration of B when the system is released from rest.

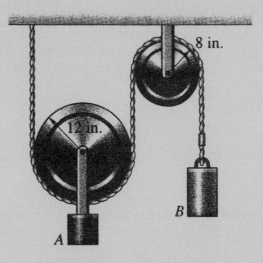

Solution

1. Imagine the combination of left pulley with attached weight A to be separated or detached from the system.

2. This combination is subjected to four external forces.

3. The right pulley is detached from weight B but still connected to its support. Hence, it is subjected to three external forces.

4. The (detached) weight B is subjected to two external forces.

5. When the system is released from rest: the left pulley is subjected to a counterclockwise angular acceleration and moves as if it was rolling on a plane surface coincident with the left part of the rope - so its center moves in a straight vertical line with upward acceleration; the right pulley is subjected to a clockwise angular acceleration and object B accelerates downward.

6. Draw the free-body diagrams in each case showing all these forces labeled with their magnitudes and directions. Include any other relevant information e.g. lengths, angles etc which may help when formulating the equations of motion (including the moment equation). Draw also the corresponding kinetic diagrams.

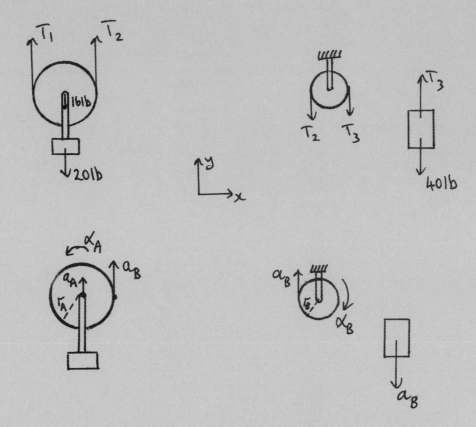

7. Write down the equation of motion in the $y-$ (vertical) direction for the weight B:

$$+\uparrow\ \ \sum F_y = ma_B : T_3 - 40 = -\left(\tfrac{40}{32.2}\right) a_B$$

8. Sum moments about the center of the right pulley and write down the moment equation of motion:

$$\circlearrowleft + \sum M_G = I_G\alpha_B : (T_2 - T_3)\left(\tfrac{8}{12}\right) = -(0.04)\,\alpha_B$$

9. For the combination of left pulley and weight A, write down the equation of motion in the $y-$ (vertical) direction:

$$+\uparrow\ \ \sum F_y = ma_A : T_1 + T_2 - 36 = \left(\tfrac{36}{32.2}\right) a A$$

and the moment equation about the center of the left pulley:

$$\circlearrowleft + \sum M_G = I_G\alpha_A : \left(\tfrac{12}{12}\right)(T_2 - T_1) = 0.24\alpha_A$$

10. You should now have 4 equations but 7 unknowns. Notice however that:

$$a_A = r_A\alpha_A = \frac{12}{12}\alpha_A,$$

$$a_B = r_B\alpha_B = \frac{8}{12}\alpha_B,$$

$$a_B = a_A + \alpha_A \times r_{B/A} - \omega_A^2 \mathbf{r}_{B/A}.$$

The final equation leads to $a_B = 2\left(\tfrac{12}{12}\right)\alpha_A$

11. Solve the 7 equations in 7 unknowns for the required acceleration $a_B : a_B = -13.2\mathbf{j}$ ft/s^2

Problem 3.34

The crate of mass m is pulled up the inclined surface by the winch. The coefficient of kinetic friction between the crate and the surface is $\mu_k = 0.4$. The moment of inertia of the drum on which the cable is wound, including the cable wound on the drum is I_A. The motor exerts a couple of magnitude M on the drum. Draw free-body and kinetic diagrams for the crate and drum

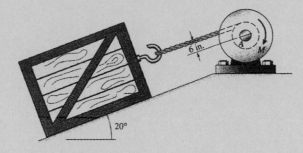

Solution

1. Imagine each of the crate and the drum to be separated or detached from the system.
2. Determine the number and types of external forces *acting on the crate* and then do the same for the drum.
3. Draw the free-body diagram of the (detached) crate/drum showing all the external forces and moments *acting on the crate/drum* labeled with their magnitudes and directions. *Assume* the sense of the vectors representing the *reactions acting on the drum.* Include any other relevant information e.g. lengths, angles etc which may help when formulating the equations of motion.
4. Indicate clearly the components of the vectors a and α for the crate and the drum, as appropriate, on separate kinetic diagrams.

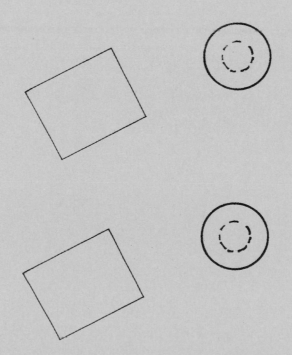

Problem 3.34

The crate of mass m is pulled up the inclined surface by the winch. The coefficient of kinetic friction between the crate and the surface is $\mu_k = 0.4$. The moment of inertia of the drum on which the cable is wound, including the cable wound on the drum is IA The motor exerts a couple of magnitude M on the drum. Draw free-body and kinetic diagrams for the crate and drum

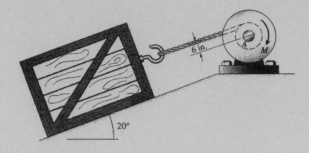

Solution

1. Imagine each of the crate and the drum to be separated or detached from the system.
2. Determine the number and types of external forces acting on the crate and then do the same for the drum.
3. Draw the free-body diagram of the (detached) crate/drum showing all the external forces and moments acting on the crate/drum labeled with their magnitudes and directions. Assume the sense of the vectors representing the reactions acting on the drum. Include any other relevant information e.g. lengths, angles etc which may help when formulating the equations of motion.
4. Indicate clearly the components of the vectors a and α for the crate and the drum, as appropriate, on separate kinetic diagrams.

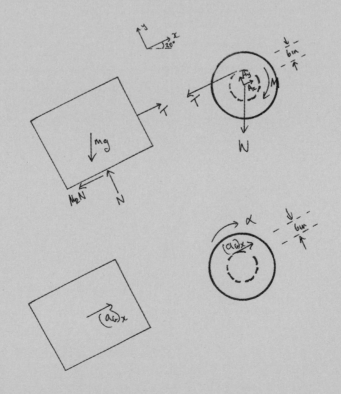

Problem 3.35

The slender bar of mass m_{bar} and the block of mass m_{block} are released from rest in the position shown. Friction is negligible. Draw free-body and kinetic diagrams of the bar and the block.

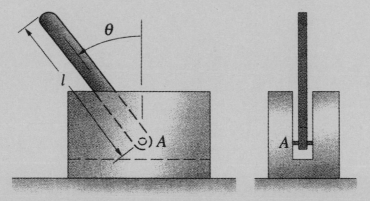

Solution

1. Imagine each of the bar and the block to be separated or detached, in turn, from the system.
2. There are four *external* forces acting on the block and three on the bar; they are not all independent.
3. Draw the free-body diagrams of the (detached) bar and block showing all these forces labeled with their magnitudes and directions. Include any other relevant information e.g. lengths, angles etc which may help when formulating the equations of motion.
4. Draw the corresponding kinetic diagrams. Be sure to indicate the components of the vectors a_G and α..

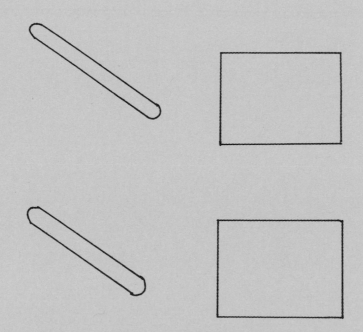

Problem 3.35

The slender bar of mass m_{bar} and the block of mass m_{block} are released from rest in the position shown. Friction is negligible. Draw free-body and kinetic diagrams of the bar and the block.

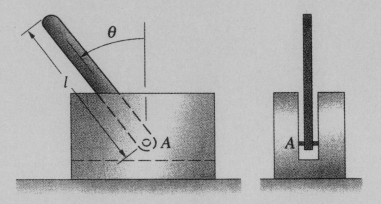

Solution

1. Imagine each of the bar and the block to be separated or detached, in turn, from the system.
2. There are four external forces acting on the block and three on the bar; they are not all independent.
3. Draw the free-body diagrams of the (detached) bar and block showing all these forces labeled with their magnitudes and directions. Include any other relevant information e.g. lengths, angles etc which may help when formulating the equations of motion.
4. Draw the corresponding kinetic diagrams. Be sure to indicate the components of the vectors a_G and α.

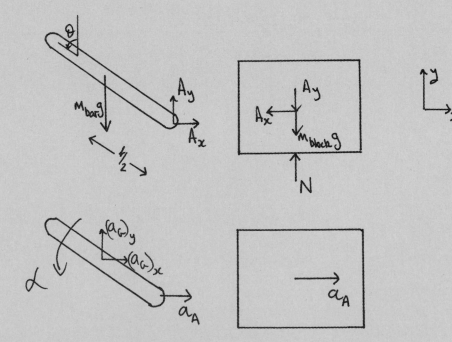

Problem 3.36

The 0.4 kg slender bar and 1 kg disk are released from rest in the position shown. If the disk rolls, draw free-body diagrams of the bar and the disk. Use these diagrams to write down the equations of motion for the disk.

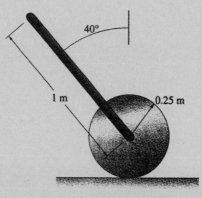

Solution

1. Imagine each of the bar and the disk to be separated or detached, in turn, from the system.

2. There are five *external* forces acting on the disk and three on the bar; they are not all independent.

3. Draw the free-body diagrams of the (detached) bar and disk showing all these forces labeled with their magnitudes and directions. Include any other relevant information e.g. lengths, angles etc which may help when formulating the equations of motion.

4. On the free-body diagrams, indicate the components of the vectors a_G and α. in each case.

5. Using the inertial coordinate system chosen on the free-body diagram write down the equations of motion for the disk:

$+\rightarrow \sum F_x = m\,(a_G)_x:$

$+\uparrow \sum F_y = m\,(a_G)_y:$

$\curvearrowleft + \sum M_G = I_G\alpha:$

Problem 3.36

The 0.4 kg slender bar and 1 kg disk are released from rest in the position shown. If the disk rolls, draw free-body diagrams of the bar and the disk. Use these diagrams to write down the equations of motion for the disk.

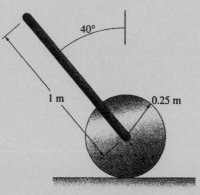

Solution

1. Imagine each of the bar and the disk to be separated or detached, in turn, from the system.

2. There are five external forces acting on the disk and three on the bar; they are not all independent.

3. Draw the free-body diagrams of the (detached) bar and disk showing all these forces labeled with their magnitudes and directions. Include any other relevant information e.g. lengths, angles etc which may help when formulating the equations of motion.

4. On the free-body diagrams, indicate the components of the vectors a_G and α. in each case.

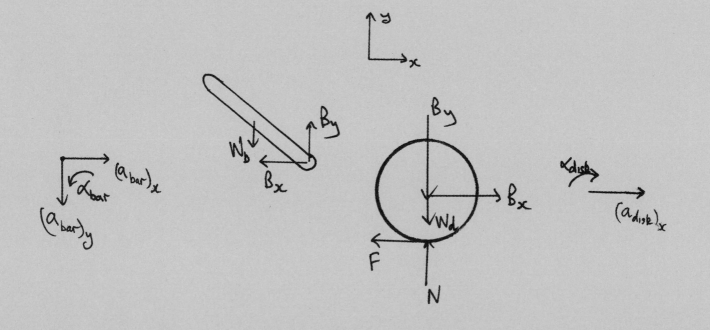

5. Using the inertial coordinate system chosen on the free-body diagram write down the equations of motion for the disk:

$+\rightarrow \sum F_x = m\,(a_G)_x : N - W_d - B_y = 0 : N - (1)\,g - B_y = 0$

$+\uparrow \quad \sum F_y = m\,(a_G)_y : B_x - F = md\,(a_G)\,x = (1)\,(a_{disk})\,x$

$\curvearrowright +\sum M_G = I_G\alpha : -(0.25)\,F = -I_G\alpha = -\left(\tfrac{1}{2}\right)(1)\,(0.25)^2\,\alpha$

Problem 3.37

Bar AB rotates counterclockwise. The slender bar BCD weighs 10 lb and the collar attached to this bar weighs 2 lb. Draw free-body and kinetic diagrams for the bar BCD. Use these diagrams to write down the equations of motion for the bar BCD. Neglect friction.

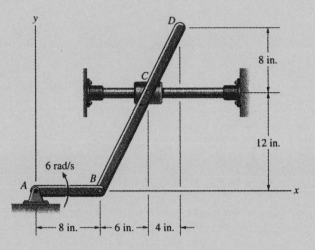

Solution

1. Imagine the bar to be separated or detached from the system.

2. There are five *external* forces acting on the bar.

3. Draw the free-body diagram of the (detached) bar showing all these forces labeled with their magnitudes and directions. Include any other relevant information e.g. lengths, angles etc which may help when formulating the equations of motion.

4. Using the inertial coordinate system chosen on the free-body diagram write down the equations of motion for the bar:

$+\rightarrow \ \sum F_x = m\,(a_G)_x$:

$+\uparrow \ \ \sum F_y = m\,(a_G)_y$:

$\curvearrowleft + \sum M_G = I_G \alpha$:

Problem 3.37

Bar AB rotates counterclockwise. The slender bar BCD weighs 10 lb and the collar attached to this bar weighs 2 lb. Draw free-body and kinetic diagrams for the bar BCD. Use these diagrams to write down the equations of motion for the bar BCD. Neglect friction.

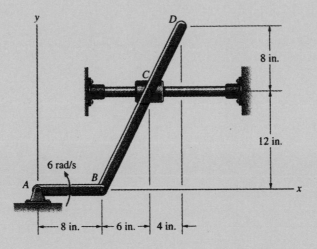

Solution

1. Imagine the bar to be separated or detached from the system.

2. There are five external forces acting on the bar.

3. Draw the free-body diagram of the (detached) bar showing all these forces labeled with their magnitudes and directions. Include any other relevant information e.g. lengths, angles etc which may help when formulating the equations of motion.

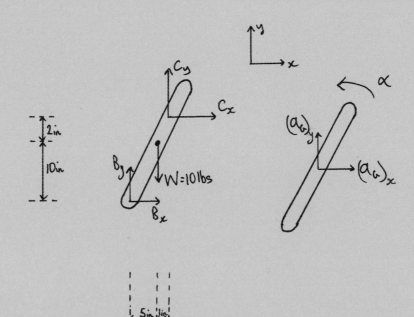

4. Using the inertial coordinate system chosen on the free-body diagram write down the equations of motion for the bar:

$$+\rightarrow \ \sum F_x = m\,(a_G)_x : B_x + C_x = \left(\tfrac{10}{32.17}\right)(a_G)_x$$

$$+\uparrow \ \ \sum F_y = m\,(a_G)_y : B_y + C_y - 10 = \left(\tfrac{10}{32.17}\right)(a_G)_y$$

$$\curvearrowleft +\sum M_G = I_G\alpha : \left(\tfrac{1}{12}\right)C_y - \left(\tfrac{5}{12}\right)B_y + \left(\tfrac{10}{12}\right)B_x - \left(\tfrac{2}{12}\right)C_x = I_G\alpha$$

Problem 3.38

Bar AB weighs 10 lb and bar BC weighs 6 lb. If the system is released from rest in the position shown, draw free-body diagrams of the bars AB and BC. The coefficient of kinetic friction between bar BC and the surface is μ_k. Draw also kinetic diagrams for each bar indicating clearly the components of the acceleration vectors.

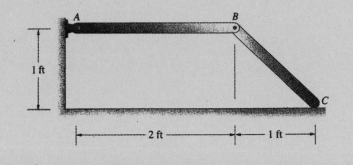

Solution

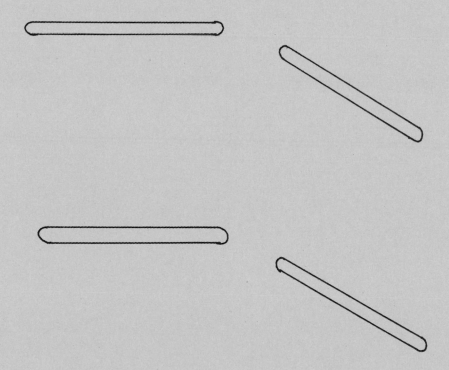

Problem 3.38

Bar AB weighs 10 lb and bar BC weighs 6 lb. If the system is released from rest in the position shown, draw free-body diagrams of the bars AB and BC. The coefficient of kinetic friction between bar BC and the surface is μ_k. Draw also kinetic diagrams for each bar indicating clearly the components of the acceleration vectors.

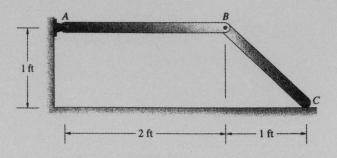

Solution

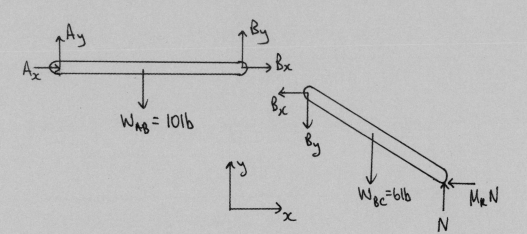

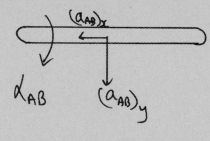

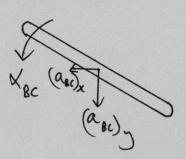

Problem 3.39

Let the total moment of inertia of the car's two rear wheels and axle be I_R and let the total moment of inertia of the two front wheels be I_F. The radius of the tires is R and the total mass of the car including the wheels is m. If the car's engine exerts a torque (couple) T on the rear wheels and the wheels do not slip, use three free-body diagrams: one of the car without its wheels and one of each detached wheel, to show that the car's acceleration is

$$a = \frac{RT}{R^2 m + IR + IF}.$$

Solution

Isolate the wheels and draw free-body diagrams of each wheel and the car without its wheels:

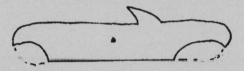

1. Using the inertial coordinate system chosen on the free-body diagram write down the following equations of motion : For the rear wheel:

$$+\rightarrow \sum F_x = m_R a :$$

$$+\uparrow \ \sum F_y = m_R (a_G)_y :$$

$$\curvearrowleft + \sum M_{Raxle} = I_R \alpha :$$

For the front wheel:

$$+\rightarrow \sum F_x = m_F a :$$

$$+\uparrow \ \sum F_y = m_F \,(a_G)_y :$$

$$\curvearrowleft + \sum M_{Faxle} = I_F \alpha :$$

For the car body: $+\rightarrow \sum F_x = m_B a :$

$$+\uparrow \ \sum F_y = m_F \,(a_G)_y :$$

2. Sum the "$x-$equations" for all three bodies to obtain a single equation:

3. From the moment equations for the wheels obtain f_F and f_R in terms of I_F, I_R, a, R and T :

4. Substitute the obtained f_F and f_R (in terms of I_F, I_R, a, R and T) into the equation obtained in 2. above, solve for a and obtain the desired result:

Problem 3.39

Let the total moment of inertia of the car's two rear wheels and axle be I_R and let the total moment of inertia of the two front wheels be I_F. The radius of the tires is R and the total mass of the car including the wheels is m. If the car's engine exerts a torque (couple) T on the rear wheels and the wheels do not slip, use three free-body diagrams: one of the car without its wheels and one of each detached wheel, to show that the car's acceleration is

$$a = \frac{RT}{R^2 m + I_R + I_F}.$$

Solution

Isolate the wheels and draw free-body diagrams of each wheel and the car without its wheels:

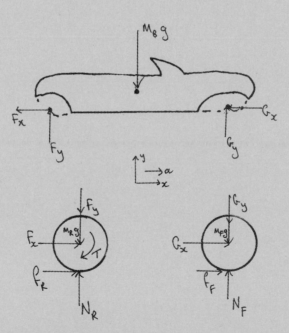

1. Using the inertial coordinate system chosen on the free-body diagram write down the following equations of motion :
   For the rear wheel:

   $$+\rightarrow \sum F_x = m_R a : F_x + f_R = m_R a$$

   $$+\uparrow\ \sum F_y = m_R (a_G)_y : N_R - m_R g - F_y = 0$$

   $$\curvearrowright + \sum M_{Raxle} = I_R \alpha : R f_R - T = I_R \alpha = I_R \left(-\frac{a}{R}\right)$$

For the front wheel:

$$+\rightarrow \sum F_x = m_F a : G_x + f_F = m_F a$$

$$+\uparrow \ \sum F_y = m_F (a_G)_y : N_F - m_F g - G_y = 0$$

$$\curvearrowleft + \sum M_{Faxle} = I_F \alpha : R F_f = I_F \alpha = I_F \left(-\frac{a}{R}\right)$$

For the car body:

$$+\rightarrow \sum F_x = m_B a : -F_x - G_x = m_B a$$

$$+\uparrow \ \sum F_y = m_F (a_G)_y : F_y + G_y = m_B g$$

2. Sum the "$x-$equations" for all three bodies to obtain a single equation:
$$f_R + f_F = (m_B + m_R + m_F) \, a = ma$$

3. From the moment equations for the wheels obtain f_F and f_R in terms of I_F, I_R, a, R and T :
$$f_F = -\frac{I_F a}{R^2}, \quad f_R = -\frac{I R a}{R^2} + \frac{T}{R}$$

4. Substitute the obtained f_F and f_R (in terms of I_F, I_R, a, R and T) into the equation obtained in 2. above, solve for a and obtain the desired result.

Problem 3.40

The object B weighs 15 lb and rests on a surface for which the coefficient of kinetic friction is μ_k. The weight of bar AB is negligible. If the person exerts a force with magnitude F on the handle, draw free-body diagrams for the handle and the object B immediately after B starts slipping. Draw also kinetic diagrams for each body.

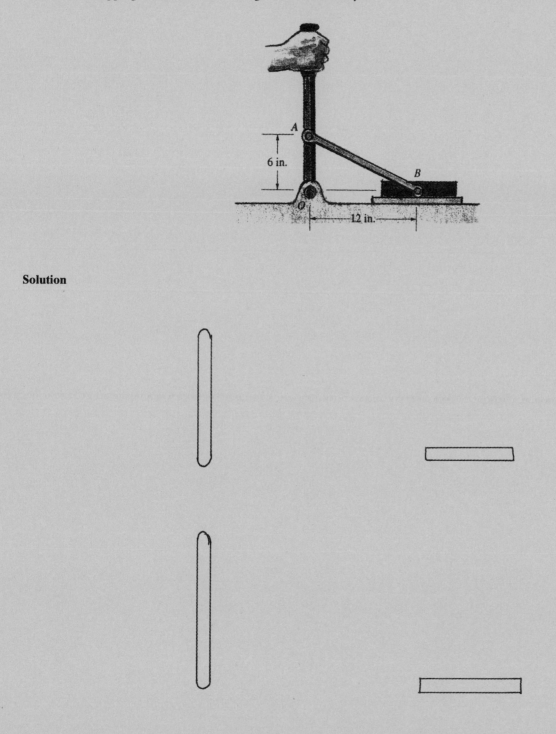

Solution

Problem 3.40

The object B weighs 15 lb and rests on a surface for which the coefficient of kinetic friction is μ_k. The weight of bar AB is negligible. If the person exerts a force with magnitude F on the handle, draw free-body diagrams for the handle and the object B immediately after B starts slipping. Draw also kinetic diagrams for each body.

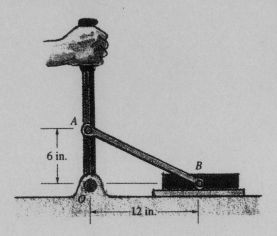

Solution

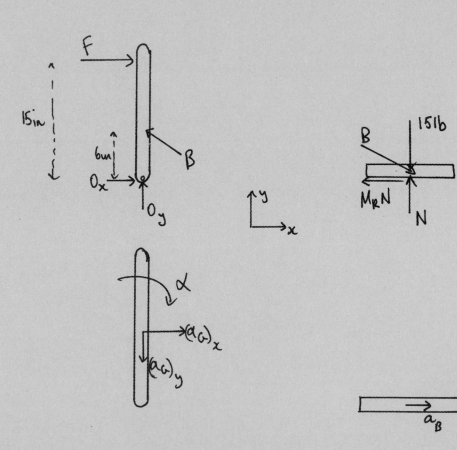

Problem 3.41

Bars OQ and PQ each weigh 6 lb. The weight of the collar P and the friction between the collar and the horizontal bar are negligible. If the system is released from rest with $\theta = 45°$, draw free-body and kinetic diagrams for each bar.

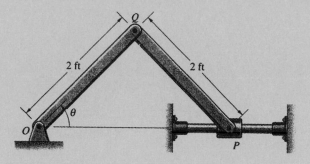

Solution

Problem 3.41

Bars OQ and PQ each weigh 6 lb. The weight of the collar P and the friction between the collar and the horizontal bar are negligible. If the system is released from rest with $\theta = 45°$, draw free-body and kinetic diagrams for each bar.

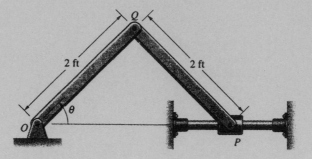

Solution

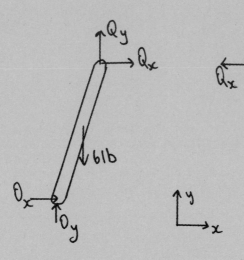

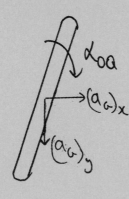

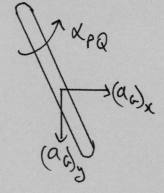

Problem 3.42

The 4 kg slender bar is pinned to 2 kg sliders at A and B. If friction is negligible and the system is released from rest in the position shown, draw:

 i. A free-body diagram of bar AB.
 ii. A free-body diagram of the slider at A.
 iii. A free-body diagram of the slider at B.
 iv. A kinetic diagram of bar AB with sliders attached.

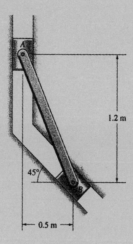

Solution

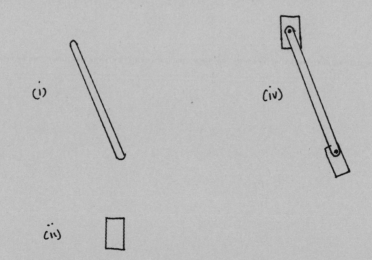

Problem 3.42

The 4 kg slender bar is pinned to 2 kg sliders at A and B. If friction is negligible and the system is released from rest in the position shown, draw:

  i. A free-body diagram of bar AB.

  ii. A free-body diagram of the slider at A.

  iii. A free-body diagram of the slider at B.

  iv. A kinetic diagram of bar AB with sliders attached.

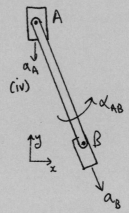

Solution

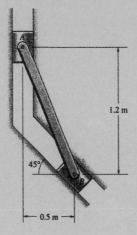

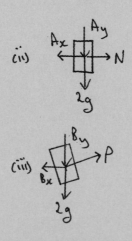

Problem 3.43

The mass of the slender bar is m and the mass of the homogeneous disk is 4 m. The system is released from rest in the position shown. If the disk rolls and the coefficient of kinetic friction between the bar and the horizontal surface is μ_k , draw free-body diagrams for the disk and the bar.

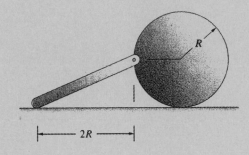

Solution

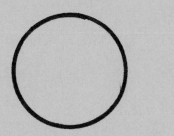

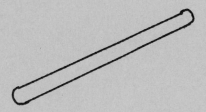

Problem 3.43

The mass of the slender bar is m and the mass of the homogeneous disk is 4 m. The system is released from rest in the position shown. If the disk rolls and the coefficient of kinetic friction between the bar and the horizontal surface is μ_k, draw free-body diagrams for the disk and the bar.

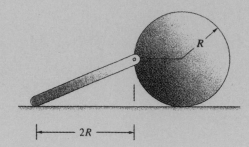

Solution

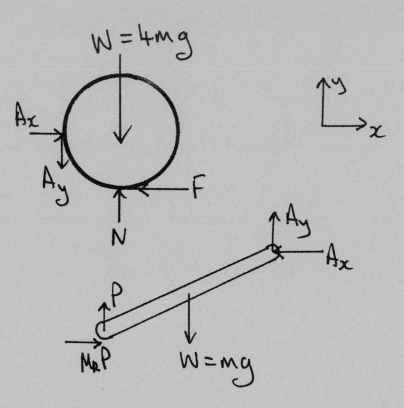

Problem 3.44

The pulleys can turn freely on their pin supports . They are initially stationary, and at $t = 0$ a constant counterclockwise moment of magnitude M is applied at pulley A. If motion is in the horizontal plane, draw free-body diagrams for each of the pulleys. Denote the upper and lower belts by the subscripts U and L, respectively.

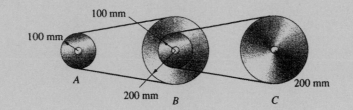

Solution

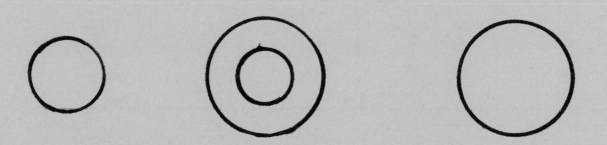

Problem 3.44

The pulleys can turn freely on their pin supports · They are initially stationary, and at $t = 0$ a constant counterclockwise moment of magnitude M is applied at pulley A. If motion is in the horizontal plane, draw free-body diagrams for each of the pulleys. Denote the upper and lower belts by the subscripts U and L, respectively.

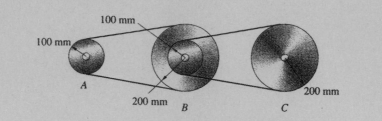

Solution

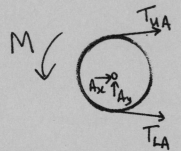

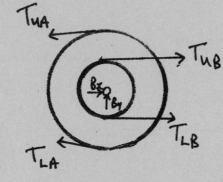

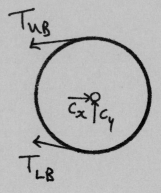

A   B   C

Problem 3.45

Pulley *A* weighs 4 lb and pulley *B* weighs 1 lb. If the system is released from rest, draw free-body diagrams for each pulley and the 16 lb weight.

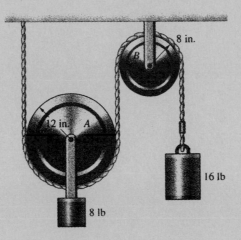

Solution

Problem 3.45

Pulley A weighs 4 lb and pulley B weighs 1 lb. If the system is released from rest, draw free-body diagrams for each pulley and the 16 lb weight.

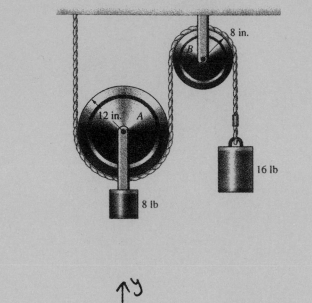

Solution

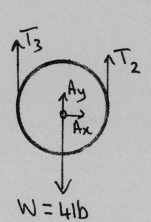

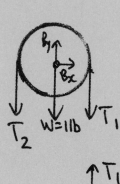

Problem 3.46

Model the excavator's arm ABC as a single rigid body. Its mass is 1200 kg and the moment of inertia about its center of mass is $I_G = 3600$ kg·m². If point A is stationary, the angular velocity of the arm is zero and the angular acceleration of the arm is 1.0 rad/s² counterclockwise, use a free-body diagram of the arm to find what force the vertical hydraulic cylinder exerts on the arm at B.

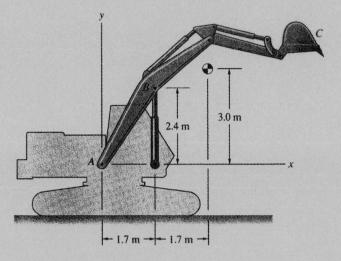

Solution

First draw the free-body diagram for the arm.

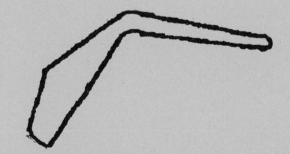

Next,

1. Find the distance d from A to the center of mass:

2. The moment of inertia about the point A is:

3. Sum moments about A (why?):

$$\curvearrowleft + \sum M_A = I_A \alpha :$$

4. Substitute the given value of α and solve for the required force magnitude:

Problem 3.46

Model the excavator's arm ABC as a single rigid body. Its mass is 1200 kg and the moment of inertia about its center of mass is $I_G = 3600$ kg·m^2. If point A is stationary, the angular velocity of the arm is zero and the angular acceleration of the arm is 1.0 rad/s^2 counterclockwise, use a free-body diagram of the arm to find what force the vertical hydraulic cylinder exerts on the arm at B.

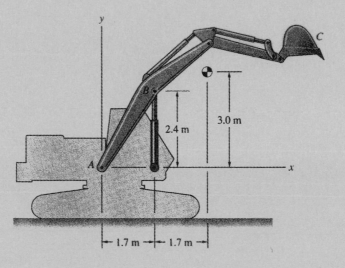

Solution

First draw the free-body diagram for the arm.

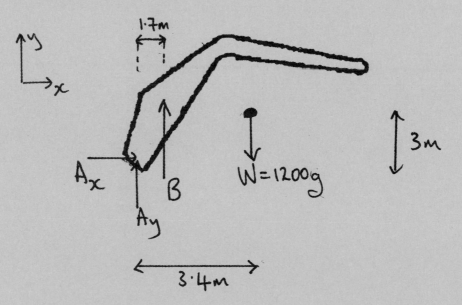

Next,

1. Find the distance d from A to the center of mass:
$$d = \sqrt{(3.4)^2 + (3)^2} = 4.53 \text{ m}$$

2. The moment of inertia about the point A is:
$$I_A = I_G + d^2 m = 28270 \text{ kg·m}^2$$

3. Sum moments about A (why? - eliminates pin-reactions):

$$\circlearrowleft + \sum M_A = I_A \alpha : 1.7B - 3.4mg = I_A \alpha$$

4. Substitute the given value of α and solve for the required force magnitude: $B = 40170$ N.

Problem 3.47

The slender bars each weigh 4 lb and are 10 in long. The homogeneous plate weighs 10 lb. If the system is released from rest in the position shown, draw free-body diagrams for each of the bars and the plate.

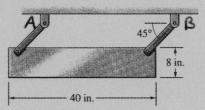

Solution

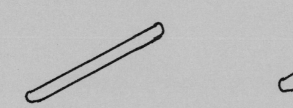

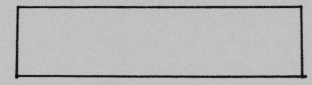

Problem 3.47

The slender bars each weigh 4 lb and are 10 in long. The homogeneous plate weighs 10 lb. If the system is released from rest in the position shown, draw free-body diagrams for each of the bars and the plate.

Solution

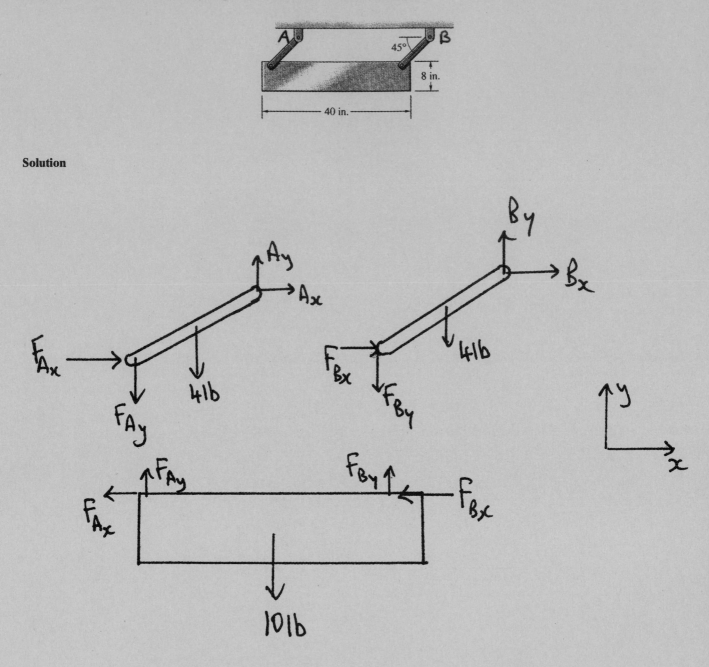

Problem 3.48

Each of the go-carts front wheels weighs 5 lb. The two rear wheels and rear axle form a single rigid body weighing 40 lb. The total weight of the go-cart and rider is 240 lb (the location of the center of mass of the go-cart and driver *not including* the front wheels or the rear wheels and axle is shown). The engine exerts a torque of magnitude M on the rear axle. Draw free-body diagrams for: (i) the rear wheel assembly (ii) the front wheel assembly and (iii) the frame.

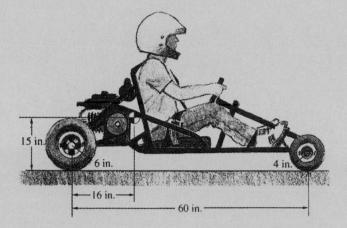

15 in.

6 in.

4 in.

16 in.

60 in.

Solution

(iii)

(i)

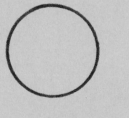

(ii)

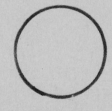

Problem 3.48

Each of the go-carts front wheels weighs 5 lb. The two rear wheels and rear axle form a single rigid body weighing 40 lb. The total weight of the go-cart and rider is 240 lb (the location of the center of mass of the go-cart and driver not including the front wheels or the rear wheels and axle is shown). The engine exerts a torque of magnitude M on the rear axle. Draw free-body diagrams for: (i) the rear wheel assembly (ii) the front wheel assembly and (iii) the frame.

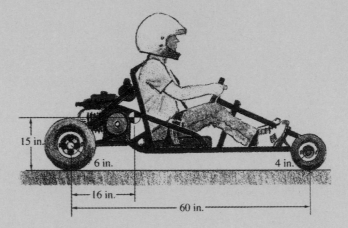

Solution

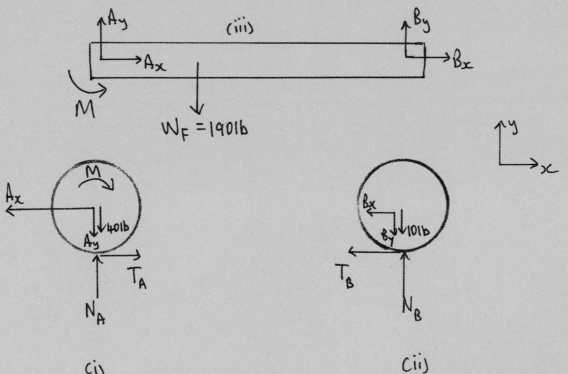

Problem 3.49

Bar AB rotates in the counterclockwise direction. The masses of the slender bars BC and CDE are 2 kg and 3.6 kg, respectively. The $y-$axis points upward. Draw free-body diagrams for each of the bars BC and CDE at this instant.

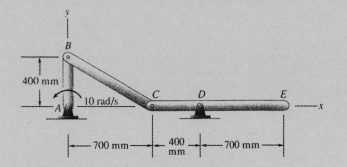

Solution

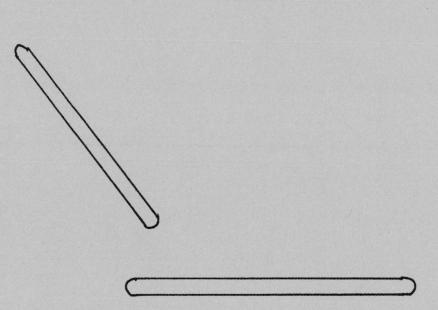

Problem 3.49

Bar AB rotates in the counterclockwise direction. The masses of the slender bars BC and CDE are 2 kg and 3.6 kg, respectively. The y−axis points upward. Draw free-body diagrams for each of the bars BC and CDE at this instant.

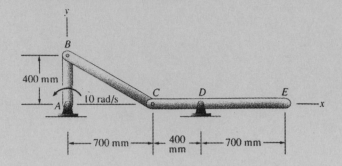

Solution

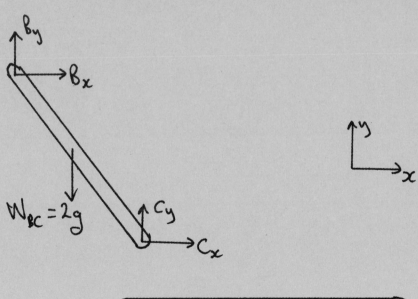

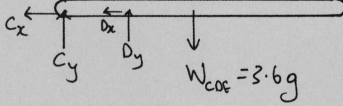

Problem 3.50

The system is stationary at the instant shown. The net force exerted on the piston by the exploding fuel-air mixture and friction is 5 kN to the left. A clockwise couple $M = 200$ N·m acts on the crank AB. The mass of the connecting rod BC is 0.36 kg and its center of mass is 40 mm from B on the line from B to C. the mass of the piston is 4.6 kg. Neglect the gravitational forces on the crank and connecting rod. Draw free-body diagrams for:

  i. The crank

 ii. The connecting rod.

iii. The piston.

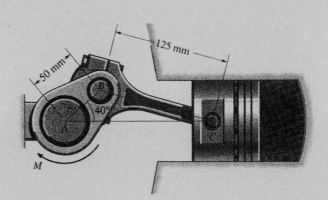

Solution

(1)

(ii)

(iii)

126 Chap. 3 Problems

Problem 3.50

The system is stationary at the instant shown. The net force exerted on the piston by the exploding fuel-air mixture and friction is 5 kN to the left. A clockwise couple $M = 200$ N·m acts on the crank AB. The mass of the connecting rod BC is 0.36 kg and its center of mass is 40 mm from B on the line from B to C. the mass of the piston is 4.6 kg. Neglect the gravitational forces on the crank and connecting rod. Draw free-body diagrams for:

  i. The crank
 ii. The connecting rod.
iii. The piston.

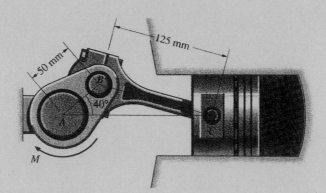

Solution

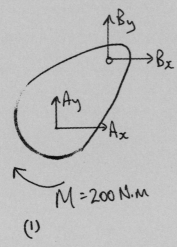

(1)

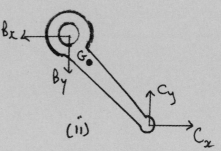

(ii)

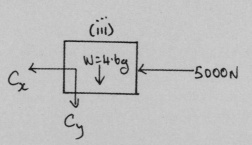

(iii)

Appendix

Questions to Accompany Working Model Simulations—Dynamics

2.1

1. For the lowest starting velocity, the spacecraft moves out until the velocity is zero. This means that the spacecraft did not make it to the Moon's distance. How far did it get?
2. Find the starting velocity that just gets you to the Moon. You can use trial and error or you can use your analysis to find the answer quickly.
3. Calculate the escape velocity of Earth at the initial distance and set this as the initial velocity. Do you really want to wait for the simulation to complete?
4. What happens for initial velocities higher than escape velocity? See what happens with the simulation.

2.2

∗ To answer all of these questions, you need to set values for A, B, and C.

1. How would you climb vertically?
2. How would you descend vertically?
3. How would you fly horizontally?
4. How would you maximize your velocity at the end of the time segment? Why does this happen? State your explanation in a short paragraph.
5. How is the size of the closed curve related to the amplitude of the motion of the slider on the vertical bar?

2.3

∗ Use the slider at the bottom of the simulation to move forward and back in time in the simulation.

1. For the lowest value of acceleration, what is the velocity as the car enters the turn? as it completes the turn?
2. For the highest value of acceleration, what is the velocity as the car enters the turn? as it completes the turn?
3. Why is there a jump in acceleration as the car enters the turn? Why is the jump larger when the linear acceleration is higher?
4. What is the highest value of total acceleration experienced by the car with the highest linear acceleration? Where does this occur? What is the value of the linear acceleration at this point?

2.4

1. What combination of motor velocity and spring constant leads to the largest radius of motion in this simulation?
2. What combination of motor velocity and spring constant leads to the smallest radius of motion in this simulation?
3. For a motor velocity of 30 deg/s, what spring constant leads to the largest radius of motion in this simulation?
4. For a motor velocity of 30 deg/s, what spring constant leads to the smallest radius of motion in this simulation?
5. With smaller velocities for the motor, why does the simulation stop after the bar has turned through smaller angles?

2.5

1. What set(s) of values for A and B result in no motion at all?
2. What set(s) of values for A and B result in motion with the highest frequency?
3. What set(s) of values for A and B result in motion with the largest amplitude of oscillation?
4. What set(s) of values for A and B result in motion with the largest magnitude of velocity?
5. What set(s) of values for A and B result in motion with the largest magnitude of acceleration?
6. Compare the motion with $B = 15$ to $B = 60$. Use $A = 30$ in both cases. What can you say about the frequencies and amplitudes of the motions.

3.1

1. Compare the accelerations on the driver in the following cases: (largest spring constant, largest damping) and (smallest spring constant, smallest damping)
2. Compare the accelerations on the driver in the following cases: (largest spring constant, largest damping) and (largest spring constant, smallest damping)
3. Compare the accelerations on the driver in the following cases: (smallest spring constant, largest damping) and (smallest spring constant, smallest damping)
4. Based on what you learned in the comparisons above, recommend values for the spring constant and damping constant for the SUV. Write a paragraph defending your choices.

3.2

1. Choose values for the coefficient of friction and the angular acceleration so that the block slides inward on the bar. Write these values down.
2. Choose values for the coefficient of friction and the angular acceleration so that the block slides outward on the bar Write these values down.
3. Choose values for the coefficient of friction and the angular acceleration so that the block initially slides outward on the bar and then slides inward. Write these values down.
4. Develop an analysis of the motion of the block and bar and verify the results you obtained in problems 1, 2, and 3, above.

3.3

∗ Run the model with coefficients of kinetic friction of 0.0, 0.05, 0.10, 0.15, 0.20, 0.25, and 0.30. Leave all of the plots on the graph.

1. Draw free body diagrams and calculate the acceleration, velocity, and position for the case where the coefficient of kinetic friction is 0.10. Evaluate at t = I sec and use this to positively identify the location of the marks on the horizontal time scale.
2. Plot the positions for all of the cases at $t = 1$ second versus the coefficient of kinetic friction. (Do this plot on graph paper and sketch the curve between the points)
3. Plot the velocities for all of the cases at $t = 1$ second versus the coefficient of kinetic friction. (Do this plot on graph paper and sketch the curve between the points)
4. Plot the accelerations for all of the cases at $t = 1$ second versus the coefficient of kinetic friction. (Do this plot on graph paper and sketch the curve between the points).
5. Develop a new plot of your own choosing for this problem.

3.4

1. Run the model with the initial velocity = −100 ft/s. Determine the terminal (steady state) velocity of the skydiver from the plot. Write this number down. Also write down the skydiver's time of flight.

2. Start the skydiver with an initial velocity of zero and verify the terminal (steady state) velocity found above. Again record your final values.

3. Start the skydiver with an initial velocity approximately equal to the terminal velocity found above and use this case to get a better value for the terminal velocity.

4. The parachutist starts 150 ft above the ground with the given initial velocity and the parachute fully opened. The horizontal scale on the plot is time in seconds. Use the information on the plot to make a graph of Time of flight versus Initial Velocity of the skydiver. (Do this plot on graph paper and sketch the curve between the points).

3.5

∗ Run this model for angular velocity values of 10, 20, 30, 40, 50, and 60 rpm. Leave all of the lines generated plotted on the grid.

1. Develop a plot of the magnitude of the collar's velocity at $t = 2$ seconds versus the Angular velocity of the bar. (Do this plot on graph paper and sketch the curve between the points)

2. Do an analysis of the problem and verify that your plot should be as it is.

4.1

1. For a coefficient of kinetic of friction of 1.0, find the combination of masses for A and B that results in the largest value of velocity for crate A as it reaches the 400 mm point down the plane.

2. For a coefficient of kinetic of friction of 0.5, find the combination of masses for A and B that results in the largest value of velocity for crate A as it reaches the 400 mm point down the plane.

3. For a coefficient of kinetic of friction of 0.0, find the combination of masses for A and B that results in the largest value of velocity for crate A as it reaches the 400 mm. point down the plane.

4.2

∗ Set initial radius = 6000 miles and initial speed = 5 mi/s. Run the model and press run again when the model stops running. This should give provide 540 degrees of motion on the plot.

1. From the plot, find the approximate period of the orbit.

2. Based on the fact that angular momentum is conserved in the orbit, explain the two humps per orbit in the VR plot. Now set initial radius = 6000 miles and initial speed to 5.40 mi/sec.

3. From the plot, what is the approximate period of this orbit? Run several cases for low and high initial radii, varying velocities at each initial radius.

4. Explain in words why the effect of changing initial velocity by 0.4 mi/s is MUCH greater with a higher initial radius than with a lower initial radius.

4.3

1. Set the initial speed to 80 mph and run the model for cars with weights ranging between 1500 lb and 5000 lb. Record the total (stopping) distance for each case. Plot total distance vs weight of car. (Do this plot on graph paper and sketch the curve between the points).

2. Set the initial speed to 20 mph and run the model for cars with weights ranging between 1500 lb and 5000 lb. Record the total (stopping) distance for each case. Plot total distance vs weight of car. (Do this plot on graph paper and sketch the curve between the points).

3. Set the initial speed to 40 mph and run the model for cars with weights ranging between 1500 lb and 5000 lb. Record the total (stopping) distance for each case. Plot total distance vs weight of car. (Do this plot on graph paper and sketch the curve between the points).

4. Set the weight of the car to 5000 lb and vary the initial speed between 20 mph and 80 mph. Record the total (stopping) distances. Plot total distance vs the initial speed of the car. (Do this plot on graph paper and sketch the curve between the points).

4.4

∗ Run this model for several pellet masses. Use the slider at the bottom to back the model up and find the point at which the green normal force disappears (where the pellet leaves the surface). Record the angle and pellet velocity corresponding to this point in each case. Keep all of the lines on the graph as you run the cases.

1. What does the alignment of the points where kinetic and potential energies cross for the various cases signify?
2. Do an analysis of this problem and determine whether the angles where the various pellets leave the surface should be the same. Does the model support your findings?

5.1

1. Try to get the two weights to bounce away from each other after collision with the coefficient of restitution set to zero. Try many combinations of masses and initial velocities. What did you learn. Write a paragraph stating your findings.
2. Using a coefficient of restitution of zero, investigate various combinations of masses and initial velocities which result in collisions in which the velocity after the collision is zero. Create one such collision with the A moving initially at 2 ft / s and B moving initially at 4 ft/s.
3. Under what conditions do the collision of A and B merely reverse the signs of the velocities of A and B after the collision .
4. Under what conditions do the collision of A and B have A and B merely trading velocities during the collision?

5.2

∗ Run the model for meteor masses varying from the lowest to the highest available values. Record the values of the meteor masses and the resulting beta angles.

1. Plot the beta angle versus meteor mass. (Do this plot on graph paper and sketch the curve between the points).
2. From the plot generated above, find the meteor mass which will produce a beta angle of 15 degrees. Run the simulation to verify your answer for this situation.
3. From the plot generated above, find the meteor mass which will produce a beta angle of 10 degrees. Run the simulation to verify your answer for this situation.

5.3

1. How is this problem related to conservation of angular momentum.
2. Locate the center of mass of the system when the tether is short and when it is long.
3. What is the number of g's experienced by the large satellite with the short tether and with the long tether?
4. What is the number of g's experienced by the small satellite with the short tether and with the long tether?

6.1

1. At what position of the slider on the circular bar does the angular acceleration of bar BC to reach its most negative value?

6.2

1. What happens when the line along DE passes through B?

6.3

1. Set motor velocities B and C to zero and let motor velocity $A = 2$. Describe the ensuing motion of point D.
2. Set motor velocities A and C to zero and let motor velocity $B = 1$ rad/s. Describe the ensuing motion of point D.
3. Set motor velocities A and B to zero and let motor velocity $C = 4$ rad/s. Describe the ensuing motion of point D.
4. Set the motor velocities $A = 2$ rad/s, $B = -2$ rad/s, and $C = -2$ rad/s. Describe the ensuing motion of point D.
5. Try various combinations of extreme rates for the three motors. Record your inputs and describe the ensuing motion of point D in each case.

7.1

1. What happens when the Bar mass is maximum and the block Mass is minimum. Describe the motion in words.
2. What happens when the Bar mass is minimum and the block Mass is maximum. Describe the motion in words.
3. What happens when the both the Bar mass and the block Mass are at their minimum values. Describe the motion in words.
4. What happens when the both the Bar mass and the block Mass are at their maximum values. Describe the motion in words.

7.2

1. Keep pressing the Run button on this model and watch the scaling change on the plot. Watch what happens when the top slider jams in the comer.

8.1

1. In all cases, the angular velocity of AB vs angle of AB plot is a closed curve. What does this mean?
2. Which combination of masses and spring constant gives the smallest closed curve? Why does this happen? State your explanation in a short paragraph.
3. Which combination of masses and spring constant gives the largest closed curve?
4. How would you maximize your horizontal velocity at the end of the 10 second time segment with zero vertical velocity?

8.2

1. Set the spring constant at its maximum value and vary the mass of the bar. Run the simulation. You may have to press Run more than once to get the bar's angle of rotation to go to its maximum value. Record the values of the bar's mass and its corresponding maximum angle of rotation. Plot maximum angle of rotation vs the mass of the bar. (Do this plot on graph paper and sketch the curve between the points).
2. Set the spring constant at its minimum value and vary the mass of the bar. Run the simulation. You may have to press Run more than once to get the bar's angle of rotation to go to its maximum value. Record the values of the bar's mass and its corresponding maximum angle of rotation. Plot maximum angle of rotation vs the mass of the bar. (Do this plot on graph paper and sketch the curve between the points).

8.3

1. Run the model for various initial velocities of bar A. Record the initial velocities and the resulting angular velocities of A bonded to B. Plot the angular velocity after the collision versus the initial velocity of bar A. (Do this plot on graph paper and sketch the curve between the points).
2. Create an analysis of this problem and verify two points on the graph produced above.

8.4

1. For what range of possible initial velocities does the student avoid the collision?
2. Assume maximum masses for both vehicles. For a coefficient of restitution of 0.5, find the initial speed for the student's car that will lead to an after collision speed of 0.8 km/hr for the university president's car.
3. Assume the maximum mass for the president's car and let the mass of the student's car vary between 900 kg and 1260 kg. Run simulations with the initial velocity of A being set at 5 km/hr and the coefficient of restitution set at 0.3. Record the magnitude of the velocity of the president's car after the collision and its corresponding angular velocity. Plot the magnitude of the post collision linear velocity of the president's car versus the mass of the student's car. (Do this plot on graph paper and sketch the curve between the points).
4. For the situation immediately above, plot the magnitude of the post collision angular velocity of the president's car versus the mass of the student's car. (Do this plot on graph paper and sketch the curve between the points).
5. Develop a new plot of your own choosing for this problem.

10.1

1. What combination of damping, mass, and spring constant give the smallest displacement of the center of mass in the y direction?

2. What combination of damping, mass, and spring constant give the largest displacement of the center of mass in the y direction?

3. Compare the motions of the system having (weakest spring, largest mass, and highest damping) with the system having (strongest spring, largest mass, and highest damping). Write a paragraph explaining the differences in the two systems.

4. Compare the motions of the system having (weakest spring, largest mass, and highest damping) with the system having (weakest spring, largest mass, and lowest damping). Write a paragraph explaining the differences in the two systems.